THE
FOOTBALL
CRÓNICAS

THE
FOOTBALL
CRÓNICAS

EDITED by JETHRO SOUTAR
AND TIM GIRVEN

 Ragpicker Press

(1) Mario Murillo

(5) Pablo Corso

(6) Surya Lecona Moctezuma

(2) Alberto Salcedo Ramos

(3) Marco Avilés

(4) Álex Ayala Ugarte

(8) Clara Becker

(7) Leonardo Haberkorn

(11) Hernán Iglesias Illa

(9) Juan Pablo Meneses

(10) Wilmer Urrelo Zárate

(12) Agustín del Moral Tejeda

(14) Diego Trelles Paz

(13) José Pérez Reyes

(15) Vinicius Jatobá

THE FOOTBALL CRÓNICAS

First published in 2014 by Ragpicker Press Ltd
70 Frederick Place, London, SE18 7BH

Royalties from sales of this book will be donated to
The Bottletop Foundation

ISBN 978-0-9929161-0-7
eBook ISBN 978-0-9929161-1-4

Text design, typesetting and eBook by Tetragon, London
Copyedited by Bryan Karetnyk
Proofread by Ian Howe
Cover design by Finn Dean

Printed and bound by T.J. International, Padstow, Cornwall

CONTENTS

Extracto

An extract from a creative non-fiction book

Cuentos/Contos

Three works of fiction

FOREWORD

Tim Vickery

Dying is not in my plans at the moment, but with fifty not far away I might have to deal with the fact that it just could happen one day. If and when it does, then the epitaph I want on my gravestone will probably be this: "Football is a universal language that we speak with different accents."

We take the extraordinary global success of the game for granted. Explanations tend to focus on the fact that all shapes and sizes can play, the low barriers to entry and football's simplicity. Often over-looked is that such simplicity masks a dazzling and fascinating com-plexity; the player on the ball can pass forward, backward, sideways, in the air or on the ground, long or short. He does not even need to pass. He can run with the ball, go for a dribble. The range of options is immense. It would seem evident that a strong cultural content exists in the way that the options are chosen. The clear conclusion is that different cultures can express themselves through their approach to the game. As you live, they say, so you play football.

And so you watch it, react to it, judge it, conceptualise it and build narratives around it. The truth, perhaps, lies not in accuracy but in artful interpretation – especially when it comes to South American football. Pre-1970, World Cups were not broadcast live. Brazil accompanied its first two triumphs, in 1958 and 1962, glued to the enthusiastic reports of its radio journalists. A couple of days later the tape of the game arrived, from Sweden and Chile respectively. With all due solemnity it was carried off the plane and copied for mass release. There were times when the images of the match did not quite live up to the colourful accounts that people had heard on the radio. Nelson Rodrigues, a football fanatic and one of the country's leading writers, had the perfect response: the tape was wrong. The truth was to be found in the creative emotion of the radio reports.

Those triumphs for Brazil, like those for Argentina and Uruguay, were the nation represented to the world. The importance of football to the Southern Cone can be separated into three phases: the game was introduced by the British, and arrived full of first-world prestige; it swiftly moved down the social scale, on the way being reinterpreted by the locals, who replaced the straight-line-running, muscular Christianity of the British with something more sinuous and balletic; this reinterpretation led to international triumphs and recognition for a region starved of such things. That makes football a powerful force, the nation in boots.

But football in South America also has the capacity to subvert. This is a region where notions of hierarchy are hugely important – especially in Brazil. From Leônidas da Silva to Romário, a strong part of the game's appeal has been the way it permits a pawn to become a king. It is hard to think of any other field of human activity that would have given Diego Maradona the chance to achieve prominence. Football, then, can sustain ideas of the nation at the same time as it subverts some of its pillars. How to deal with these contradictions? It is probably no surprise that South American football drinks from the rich literary tradition of the *crónica* – a hybrid form, sufficiently flexible to play host to a delicious row between myth and reality, truth and fiction, opinion and fact, the personal and the collective. The football *crónica* is a chunk of literature to be discussed and debated in a café or bar – and this collection is a worthy addition to a lively tradition.

Mario Murillo was born in La Paz, Bolivia, on August 7, 1980. He teaches at Universidad Mayor de San Andrés and the Universidad Católica Boliviana. He has had two books published, *La bala no mata sino el destino: Una crónica de la insurrección popular de 1952 en Bolivia* (Plural, 2012) and *La pelota no se mancha: Una etnografía de la Liga Deportiva El Tejar en Bolivia* (IDIS, 2013), as well as football *crónicas* and articles in a range of compendiums and magazines. He was a screenwriter and assistant director on the documentary film *La bala no mata* (Fundación Grupo Ukamau, 2012) and is a member of the anarco-ch'ixi group *El Colectivo 2*.

'The Goal in the Back of Beyond' ('*Ahí donde se grita gol*') was first published in 2011 in *Bolivia a toda costa: Crónicas de un país de ficción*, an anthology co-published by the El Cuervo and Nuevo Milenio publishing houses.

THE GOAL IN THE BACK OF BEYOND

Mario Murillo

Translated by Jethro Soutar

I get to the ground at nine-thirty, half an hour early. The players have been told to be at Tembladeri by ten, when the bus will leave for the airport. Diego and I are in charge of the delegation. It's always amusing to see the look of surprise on people's faces – airport staff, the other team's directors, both sets of supporters – when they see two casually dressed young men leading the Club Bolívar delegation. In a country as adult-centric as Bolivia, people like us are usually given menial tasks to perform, until we become real men – "experience" being some kind of right of passage – capable of handling real jobs. Diego and I are lucky, maybe too lucky.

This match is crucial. With three league games to go, we have to win to stand any chance of getting into the play-offs. Football is a strange business. Despite all the effort and hard work, despite the dazzling new signings and the return of Jorge Carlos Habegger as manager, the team never gelled and now we need a miracle to qualify. We're going to Potosí in search of that miracle.

No players have arrived yet. I sit down by the bus and watch the kit man and the physio go through their preparations. They load up boots, shirts, tracksuits, drinks, balls. I light a cigarette and wait for the first player to show. I'd like to talk to one of them before getting on the bus, but it's impossible to establish any kind of equal relationship: they see me as a "director"; I see them as heroes. When I told a friend, Gabriel Guzmán, that I was thinking of joining the management committee, he warned me: "You'll never be the same again. You'll never have that same relationship with your team, not like it is now, straight from the heart. That's the price you'll pay, there's no escaping it. But if you think it's worth it, fine, go ahead." As I sit waiting to board the bus and travel with the team, I ask myself whether I've yet paid that price? I don't think so: my relationship with the game is still based on passion and raw emotion. But even thinking about it makes me uneasy, and although I hope I'm mistaken, I wonder whether my friend's predictions are starting to come true.

The players arrive in ones and twos. They greet me from afar. My sense of awe prevents me from going over to them, meaning relations remain cold and formal. I would kill to be thought of as a mate, but it seems impossible. The distance is too great. Diego arrives. Now he is a mate. We've been friends for years and have developed, I'd like to think, that sense of brotherhood that comes with true friendship. I'm pretty sure he feels the same way.

Habegger arrives. He's an interesting, somewhat complex character. He's not your typical uncultured manager, the sort who knows his way around the tangled world of football but nothing else. Habegger has a refreshingly original football brain and a broad knowledge of the wider world to boot. Football can be rather inward looking, so it feels like a privilege to have come across him.

We board the bus. The ramshackle contraption struggles up the steep road out of La Paz. We climb out of the valley. Buildings and houses nestle in among the mountains down below, a fantasy city lost in an abyss. The atmosphere on the bus is tense. One of the players didn't turn up and the bus had to leave without him. Unpunctuality is perhaps the defining characteristic of the Bolivian people: no one is ever on time for anything. The assistant manager is especially anxious. He's spoken to the player several times on his mobile phone and the player has arranged to meet us at the airport. It's too ridiculous to contemplate that we might have to do without a key player for a match as crucial as this, because he was late and missed the flight. I'm tense too: because of waiting for the missing player, the bus was late leaving the ground. I check my watch: the flight leaves in forty-five minutes and we're nowhere near the airport. I picture the newspaper headlines: "Club Bolívar misses flight to Villa Imperial and forfeits crunch match with Real Potosí."

The traffic in El Alto is hell. There are no rules in El Alto. Or rather there are rules, but they run counter to the traditional rules of the road. Stopping at a red light is considered absurd (an angry chorus of minibus horns tells you what a mistake you've made stopping before such a meaningless symbol), as is indicating or pulling over when you need to stop. A minibus comes to a halt right in front of us, totally blocking the road, and shows no sign of going anywhere anytime soon. Joaquín Botero, centre-forward for Bolívar and the Bolivian national team, is sitting up front next to the driver, getting impatient. He sticks his head out of the window and shouts something at the top of his voice. A child's face fills with emotion. "It's Bolívar! Shift out the way, man!" the boy tells the minibus driver. The minibus quickly pulls over to one side and our bus speeds past.

I think about how that minibus wouldn't have moved for many people. A government minister or an ambulance might have been stuck there for hours. But one glimpse of our striker and the clapped-out old banger shifted quick smart. Football has that ability to speak to people in Bolivia. The game finds a way for people to identify with it, at a local and a national level. A match involving the Bolivian national team or Club Bolívar weaves a complex web of common belonging and identity. The power of the game is tremendous.

Two episodes come to mind that demonstrate this. The first was described to me by an old worker from Villa Victoria, a man who fought in the 1952 Revolution and the 2003 October Revolt: it took place before Bolivia played Brazil in a 1994 World Cup qualifier, when Bolivia qualified for the finals for the first time. The second was related to me by a university student from Los Yungas, and took place before Bolívar played Boca Juniors in the final of the Copa Sudamericana in 2004. For me, the two episodes sum up what football means to this strange and mysterious land.

First episode: the motorway that connects La Paz to the airport, 1993. The roadside is packed with people. In the distance lie Pura Pura, Villa Victoria and El Cementerio, the old factory neighbourhoods where the Amerindian workers live. The industrial labour force that comes together on a daily basis to work itself to death today gathers to party as a bus passes by on its way to Brazil. There go the players who might, after all this time, earn Bolivia a place at the World Cup finals. In the background, the factories: Soligno, Forno, Venado; the gun battles on Villa Victoria bridge; the mad scramble for the trees on El Alto, to shelter from army bullets fired from planes in those momentous days of 1952; the blaze that raged through Soligno. Today they gather not in protest or suffering, not to sacrifice their lives. Today they come together to party and celebrate, to hope. They fill the sides of the motorway, they run alongside the bus, they scream when it passes and clap furiously when they see a player at the window. Today the Bolivian flag is not painted black. Today the national anthem is sung out of joy rather than to denounce death.

Second episode: Los Yungas, La Paz, 2004. A small community travels en masse, leaving a tiny hamlet near Chulumani completely empty. The view is of immense green mountains, a panorama of incredible topography: hillside ruptures and bottomless crevasses, periodic plateaus where hardy *yungueños* build their homes. The entire population of the village – men, women, children, the elderly – parades up the hill in single file. The youngest members bring up the rear, carrying a television. One of them carries the most precious item of all: the aerial. They reach the mountain summit. Everyone sits down in front of the television. Bolívar are playing the final of the Copa Sudamericana in Buenos Aires. In the background, somewhere in the midst of the green hills, their village is a ghost town.

We get to the airport and race off the bus. The flight leaves in fifteen minutes. I can't see any way of us catching it. I run up to the check-in desk clutching everyone's identity cards. There's an ominous lack of queue. The woman behind the desk looks at me pityingly as I approach. She prepares a few gentle words to say the flight's closed. I get in first: "This is the Club Bolívar first-team squad, we've had a few problems on the road, but we're here now and we simply have to catch that plane, we've got a game against Real Potosí tomorrow, a game we must win." Her expression changes. "Bolívar?" She looks through the players' identity cards, and slowly starts to believe me. "Right. You go and pay the airport tariff while I fill out the boarding cards." I charge over to pay the airport tax and rush back to the counter. "Good luck – bring back a victory," she says, handing me the boarding cards and accepting my deepest thanks for the hundredth time.

We board the plane minutes before take-off. I pray that fate has been kind and given me a seat next to a player. Better still that it might be Leonel "Lito" Reyes or Arnulfo Valentierra. But I'm out of luck. I sit down next to an anonymous middle-aged man. We exchange not a single word. I realise afterwards that it would have made not a bit of difference: all the players have iPods, MP3s and other musical gadgets plugged into their ears, or play on their handset PlayStations and portable computers. Very few of them chat among themselves. It's said that players used to share a lot of things together. On journeys like this they'd talk and play cards or dice. Nowadays it's each to their own IT world. They share very little. This must have repercussions on the pitch. We think technology unites us, makes us equal, brings us closer together. But often it isolates us, creates distance, makes us castaways, with no need to interact with other humans. Guillermo Arriaga, the distinguished Mexican author, screenwriter of *Amores Perros*, *21 Grams*, *Babel* and *The Three Burials of Melquiades Estrada*, tells of how his students nurture relationships with women thousands of miles away on the Internet, while sitting right next to them in class is a readily available beautiful woman. Indeed.

We land in Sucre, the nearest town to Potosí with an airport. Numerous people come over to us while we're waiting for our bags, fans wanting autographs or their photos taken with the players. The players are obliging. How many photos have they had taken with strangers? How many autographs have they signed for people they don't know? After gathering up the team's huge assortment of luggage, we head for the best hotel in town. Food awaits us. The players almost always eat the same thing: chicken or vegetable soup, pasta or meat, and fruit. A frugal menu that won't interfere with their athletic performance. I imagine they must long for a good *sajta* or a spicy *pique a lo macho cochabambino*.

Diego and I have to leave promptly. We have to get to Potosí as soon as possible, for we have an important mission: to book a good restaurant that can cook a meal for the entire delegation, without revealing the meal is for Club Bolívar. The players and coaching staff will join us for the meal the following day: match day. It's no secret that many a team has fallen victim to gastronomic sabotage in the build-up to big games. It's even said that Bolivia took water from La Paz to away games in the qualifying campaign for the 1994 World Cup. To avoid any unfortunate outbreaks of pre-match food poisoning, we have to book a decent restaurant and make sure they don't know who we're booking it for.

It's already dark by the time we get to Potosí. The cold rattles my bones, but I'm happy. I've always liked Potosí, and here we are on the eve of a vital away game. We leave our things at the hotel and set off in search of a restaurant. We find a likely candidate and start to negotiate with the owner. Lunch for twenty-five people. The owner asks us who the lunch is for. We answer evasively: "A group of businessmen." She looks at us suspiciously, but relaxes when she sees we've brought cash and are prepared to pay fifty per cent up front. Mission accomplished.

I think about all the logistics that go into managing a professional football team. More than that: the logistics that go into the whole tangled network of activities and institutions involved in managing a professional football league. All that money and effort, just to organise a football competition.

It's a complicated and time-consuming business. On the other hand, all the ritual and rigmarole is mere staging: in Bolivia we imitate the structures and practices found elsewhere in professional football, but we play a different game. Matches often resemble amateur kickabouts between two neighbourhood teams. The game is slow, the players commit childish errors, the coaches order their players to fall over every other minute to stop the game, officials organise ridiculous tournaments devoid of all logic. Alison Spedding paraphrased Marx from *The Eighteenth Brumaire*, by calling her wonderful ethnography of a Bolivian women's prison *The Second Time as Farce*. She was referring to the fact that the Bolivian prison system is based on penitentiary institutions abroad, but copied in farcical fashion. This observation can be extended to many areas of Bolivian society, football among them.

It seems comedy has been present in Bolivian football right from the start. *Añejerías paceñas*, Ismael Sotomayor's delightful and exhaustive collection of La Paz anecdotes and traditions, contains the following passage:

The first football match in the city took place in 1905. The entirety of Plaza de San Pedro, or Nueva Paz, served as the sports field, or pitch, its suitability based on the fact that it was flat.

With no precise knowledge of how such matches were played in other, more advanced parts of the world, nor of the universal code of rules (in place since 1850), nobody saw any problem with putting one goal next to the cathedral and the other directly opposite, on the far side of the square, at a hugely disproportionate distance.

[...] The game began, prompting much excitement and hand clapping; the players kicked the ball enthusiastically, and they tried gallantly to score a goal, but it was difficult given the great distance they had to travel to get from one end of the pitch to the other. The match finished one-nil.

At the end of the contest, the footballers collapsed in exhaustion.

In the first match played on Bolivian soil, the goals were set so far apart it was virtually impossible to score a goal. Such a singular birth set the tone for evermore: Bolivian football continues to be high on emotion and humour. In spite of the twin pillars of professionalism and organised competition, deep down we're still trying to score goals on a pitch of slapstick proportions.

By 11:30 the next morning, after a restless night's sleep, we're stationed outside the door to the restaurant, awaiting the arrival of the players and coaching staff. They're due at the restaurant at midday. Twelve o'clock comes and goes, and there's no sign of the taxis we booked to bring them here from Sucre. We're starting to get anxious.

Another half hour passes.

Finally the caravan of taxis comes into view.

We go into the restaurant and cause quite a commotion. Adults whisper frantically to one another while children come and ask for autographs. The owner of the restaurant hurries over. "Come in, welcome," she says, and with a look that mixes understanding and reproach, adds: "Why didn't you tell me it was Bolívar? I'd have prepared something special."

After lunch we head for the hotel. Diego and I spend the afternoon in our room, talking about football. We talk about the evening's game (how the team will play, who should be in the starting line-up, who the key players will be, who might win the game for us, what needs to happen in the other fixtures to make life easier). We talk about the great teams of the past (the magical Brazil side of 1970, built on the impossible premise of four number tens playing together; Marcelo Bielsa's all-action Argentina team that peaked too soon and ended up knocked out of the 2002 World Cup at the group stage; the Dutch team of 1974, managed by Rinus Michels, the pioneer of a new footballing concept based on constant movement: the obsessive quest to lose your marker and open up space to attack into). Entire afternoons are easily spent talking about football.

Two hours before kick-off, we all go down to the lounge at the back of the hotel for the pre-match team talk. Jorge Habegger, manager of the team, commander of a thousand battles, is in frantic mode. A strange combination of nerves, excitement and emotion has taken hold of him. He stands at the front of the room and starts by talking about the opposition. He provides an overall summary of how Potosí like to play, then launches into a detailed breakdown of their tactics and formation, their main strengths and weaknesses. Then he starts on our tactics, the shapes he wants to see and how the players are to move around the pitch. He draws diagrams on a chalkboard to illustrate his points. I look at the players: they watch him with great concentration, like children before a favourite teacher. The team talk finishes with Habegger going over individual positioning at set pieces.

Before we leave for the ground, he asks for a minute of everyone's attention. He looks fiercely at the players, his eyes glowing. He stays silent for some time. Then he starts to speak, crisply at first, until his words start to tremble with emotion. He talks about what the match means, about all the people back home hoping for a victory, about the importance of playing with heart and commitment. His words rip through the atmosphere and the players visibly swell with emotion. A singular feeling of determination fills the room, albeit one tinged with anxiety and the weight of expectation.

It's said that as manager of Argentina, Marcelo Bielsa (one of the most lucid and interesting managers operating in world football today) went onto the Estadio Monumental pitch before kick-off in a 2002 World Cup qualifier against Colombia. He looked up at the stands packed with people, he listened to the cries blowing in the wind and he waited for a few moments, staring at the stillness of the pitch. He went back into the dressing room and said to his players: "In a street fight there are two types of people: those who strike, see blood and take fright; and those who strike, see blood and move in for the kill. Well, boys, I've just been out on the pitch and I'm telling you, there's blood in the air." Habegger's team talk is in a similar vein.

We board the bus and set off for the stadium. Silence reigns. The journey to the ground is often made to musical accompaniment, the players singing along and tapping their hands to lively *cumbias*. Today the loudspeakers sit silent; today nobody talks. The players stare straight ahead, concentrating so hard they almost forget to blink. Habegger's pep talk has left its mark.

The bus reaches the stadium and we head straight for the dressing room. The players start their pre-match rituals. Some start putting their kit on, others get a massage from the physio. I watch the exaggerated care with which they apply their bandaging. I could never understand this obsession with bandaging until I read Diego Maradona's autobiography. He says he used to use bandages almost as hard as plaster, to counter being kicked all the time. Footballers are our modern-day gladiators, bandages their suits of armour. All the same, the blows they take are often too hard for such flimsy shields, and bones get broken.

The players carry on getting ready. After putting their kit on, bandaging themselves, fitting shin pads inside socks and lacing up boots, they comb their hair and groom themselves in front of the mirror. The game will be dealt with in due course. For now, we're backstage, and the players want to look their best for the show. Some of them wear body thermals under their shirts. The pretext is fending off the cold, but I know it's to try and make them look more strapping and muscular. What Erving Goffman would call "impression management".

Goffman, an influential twentieth-century sociologist, argued that human beings, in the strange business of their social lives, primarily base their behaviour on what other people expect of them. The way we act, therefore, is mere performance, designed to fit in with predetermined situations and roles. A series of masks, sets and eye-catching routines. For footballers, these impression-management mechanisms are a fundamental part of the game.

Speech is the main tool used by footballers to make an impression on the opposition. Players use words to create a complex persona best suited to their quest for victory. A player once told me a story that demonstrates this point brilliantly. It took place during Bolivia's legendary 6-1 victory over Argentina in 2009. In his own words: "Sure, I've done that. We were playing against Messi here in La Paz, and I'm in the centre circle and I'm not tired but I start going huh, huh, huh [*he pants as if out of breath*]. I say to Messi, 'Shit, man, this fucking altitude's gonna kill me.' Messi starts panting too. So I'm feeding him things to put him off his game. It's all valid."

The pre-match warm-up begins. The players are put through a series of exercises in the next room. As they perform their stretches, the fitness coach shouts out motivational slogans to prepare them for battle. It's not just about warming up muscles, but rousing spirits, putting the players on a war footing. By the time they've finished, they're all highly charged, stimulated to their innermost fibres, ready for action.

They gather in the dressing room. They embrace, wish each other luck. An Argentine defender, giant frame, broad shoulders, touches Danner Pachi's head paternally. "Today's your day," he tells Pachi affectionately, staring into his eyes. The embracing multiplies, encouragement filling the room. Individual identity moulds into one rapturous, homogenous body.

We huddle together and form a circle. Lito Reyes, the team captain, stands in the middle. He pronounces a few lines that continue where Habegger left off at the hotel. Then he waits in silence for a few seconds. "Now, let us pray and thank the Lord for allowing us to do what we love. Because by playing football, we get to help our loved ones. Because we're lucky. And we pray for His protection. That we may leave the pitch in good health, that we may come to no harm out there. We pray for Him to protect us and guide us to victory." The players all start to pray. They start with the Lord's Prayer. I watch them: they all look to the heavens and pray with zeal and devotion. There is no sense of the mechanical going-through-the-motions you get at Mass. No sense of the monotony with which we used to recite the Lord's Prayer at school. We used to spit the words out almost unconsciously, habit and familiarity nullifying any sense of reverence. With the footballers it's different. They immerse themselves in the prayer, savour every last word, their eyes screwed tightly shut. They continue with a Hail Mary and deliver it – live it, even – with equal passion. If I'm ever to find God, doubtless it will be in a football dressing room before a match.

After praying, we head down the tunnel that leads onto the pitch. The roar of the terraces starts to reach us. The stadium seems to throb above our heads. The chanting gets louder. "Po-to-sí, Po-to-sí, Po-to-sí." The home team have already taken the field.

The players pause at the end of the tunnel. They stand in single file behind the captain and brace themselves one last time. A final battle cry and they run out onto the pitch. The crowds on the terraces whistle and hurl abuse at them as soon as they come into view. We are very much away from home. A handful of *bolivaristas* cheer from the other side of the pitch, tucked away in a bend of the athletics track.

Diego and I sit down on the bench with the coaching staff and substitutes. We're all very tense. We await kick-off in silence. The players take up their positions and the referee gets the game under way.

The match begins in frenetic fashion. The Real Potosí players, urged on by the crowd and their own need for victory, go boldly on the attack. They start much better than we do, dominating possession and controlling the tempo of the game. Arnulfo Valentierra, our classy Colombian midfield mastermind, a one-time Copa Libertadores winner with Once Caldas, can't get into the game, and when he does, his passing goes astray. Danner Pachi, our diminutive Bolivian international midfielder, is equally imprecise. The *potosínos* have us under the cosh and the ball barely leaves our half.

Twenty minutes in, they win a corner. It's hit long and falls to Miguel Loayza, who drills it home. A collective roar fills the atmosphere. The Potosí players celebrate just a few yards in front of us. I feel a pain in my chest and I go quiet. The stadium vibrates all around us. "It's all over," I think to myself. I look at Diego: he has his head in his hands, eyes staring at the ground. Our substitutes let fly with an incredible range of blasphemies. Habegger sits tight-lipped, his sad gaze fixed in the distance. A few moments ago he was on his feet, out of the technical area and on the touchline, practically on the pitch, shouting instructions to his players. Now he's sitting down next to us, a hostage to nerves and gloom.

The first half ends with Real Potosí 1-0 up. As we head back to the dressing room, Diego and I make frantic calculations. A draw is of no use to us. Second-half heroics seem impossible. Once again, we're facing defeat, disappointment, disillusionment. As far as I'm concerned, few heartaches are as painful as football heartaches.

The players sit down in silence. They look exhausted. Habegger is silent too and remains so for several minutes, waiting for the players to calm down and catch their breath. Then he gives another team talk. He points out the errors we've made, identifies areas of weakness in the opposition and where to work the ball in order to exploit them, how we need to move as a unit. His discourse ends with some rousing words about turning the game around and going for glory.

We retake our seats in the dugout for the second half. I'm a pessimist by nature, the sort of person who's suspicious of happiness and good fortune, and I'm totally convinced our season's over.

But, just a minute after the restart, Renato "El Tiburón" Ramos, our Chilean centre-forward, plays a lovely through-ball to Danner Pachi, who sneaks in behind Potosí's previously impenetrable defence. Pachi latches on to the ball and smashes it into the back of the net. "*Gol!*" I scream madly, melting into an embrace with Diego. The substitute players scream their heads off. Habegger celebrates with his assistants. I see Danner Pachi surrounded by teammates. The stadium is silent. There's still hope, there are still almost forty-five minutes to go.

After the goal, we take control of the game: the players grow in confidence and play with renewed energy and purpose. We keep the ball and launch wave after wave of attack. But a goal never comes and time passes swiftly by.

With twenty minutes to go, we're piling on the pressure, desperately trying to convert superior possession into goals, when they suddenly launch a counterattack. I watch helplessly as their winger bursts down the far side of the pitch and whips over a cross, as their centre-forward gets on the end of it and places the ball beyond our keeper's outstretched hand. My heart stops. The crowd cries, "*Gol!*" Then suddenly, out of nowhere, Danner Pachi comes sliding in behind the keeper and clears the ball off the line. Diego is so elated he becomes delirious. He shouts madly in my face: "Pachi has scored one and saved another: he's going to get the winner!" In these sorts of football situations, Diego often proves to be a mystic. But there's not much time left.

Play becomes bogged down as the two teams scrap it out in the middle of the park. Tiredness seems to be taking its toll on both sets of players. It's hard to get hold of the ball, let alone get it anywhere near the goal. Time advances inexorably, shrinking, each minute crashing into the next. The best way to demonstrate that time is subjective is by watching a game of football.

The whole stadium is gripped with nerves. The atmosphere is heavy, strained, anxious. Abuse rains down from the stands as collective catharsis reaches critical levels.

The team doctor tells me to go and collect the names of the players who've been selected for the anti-doping tests. I get up and walk over to the officials' technical area at the halfway line. As I cover this small stretch of ground, I'm subjected to a thousand different insults and threats. "Hippie." "Junkie." I play deaf. Football is basically catharsis, a fantasy play world where we channel the aggression and violence, devils and demons, that lurk inside us. Paul

Auster puts it another way: "Europeans have found a way to hate one another without hacking one another to pieces. This miracle goes by the name of soccer."

I'm back sitting beside Diego. A goal. Please, one measly goal. That's all we need. With fewer than five minutes left on the clock, they go on the attack. One of their players cuts into the box from the wing. One of our defenders takes the ball off his toes and plays a quick pass to Valentierra. Cerebral as ever, the Colombian sprays the ball out wide to the right, where Joaquín Botero is flying down the wing. Silence descends on the terraces again. Botero advances, gaining several yards. He looks up and chips a lovely ball into the area. "El Tiburón", a strong header of the ball, wrestles with the giant Potosí centre-backs as the ball sails through the air. The Chilean comes out on top and leaps above the defenders. We freeze on the substitutes' bench. It looks like he's going to connect with the ball. But it passes inches above his head. "Fuck."

Then suddenly I see Danner Pachi ghosting in behind the defenders' backs. The ball has overshot all of them and now little Pachi is running in to meet it, unmarked, the goal at his mercy. The moment lasts a lifetime. External reality grinds to a halt. Pachi controls the ball and looks up. He strikes the ball, placing it just inside the far post. The ball nestles in the back of the net. We run out from the dugout and onto the pitch. We run screaming until our throats are dry. Pachi is running towards us, chased by the rest of the team. We all throw ourselves on each other, a giant embrace, a human mountain. Barely conscious of what I'm doing, overcome with a feeling that transcends mere happiness, I rush towards the collective mass and launch myself on top of it. In the human pile, I find Diego. I've no idea how long we're there for. All I remember is the referee shouting at us to get off the pitch, and for the players to get back in their own half.

The remaining five minutes last an eternity. Standing at the edge of the pitch with the substitutes and coaching staff, all we can do is implore the referee to blow his whistle. Time passes slowly, but fate has rolled its last die. All we can do is wait. Suddenly, I hear the final whistle and the cries of joy multiply.

The dressing room is jubilant. The players embrace one another ecstatically. Nothing can measure up to the joy felt in that room. Habegger, a superstitious man, as all good football men are, comes over to Diego and me. "You two are to travel with us to every match. I don't want to see anyone else in the dressing room for the rest of the season." I've never felt so honoured in all my life.

The journey back to La Paz is bliss. A soundtrack of plenitude and promise hums in the background. The world has regained its shine.

I sometimes ask myself where this mad obsession comes from. My first football memories are of Bolívar and the 1986 World Cup. One of my oldest memories is of lying in bed, watching Brazil versus France. I was experiencing football's emotional highs and lows for the first time, watching the heroic deeds of Zico and Michel Platini. I recently read a lovely phrase from the Scottish poet Alastair Reid: "If a Martian were to ask what football is, a video of the Brazil–France game would be enough to convince it that football is an elevated form of artistic expression." Dead right.

Alberto Salcedo Ramos. Barranquilla, Colombia, 1963. Journalist and writer, author of numerous non-fiction books, including *La eterna parranda* and *El oro y la oscuridad* (both published by Aguilar). He is a teacher at the Fundación Nuevo Periodismo Iberoamericano and has run *crónica* workshops in several countries. His work has been included in numerous anthologies, including *Mejor que ficción* (Anagrama) and *Antología latinoamericana de crónica actual* (Alfaguara). He has been awarded the Inter American Press Association Prize for Excellence (twice), the Ortega y Gasset Prize for Journalism, the Simón Bolívar National Journalism Prize (five times) and the King of Spain's International Journalism Prize, among other distinctions. His *crónicas* have been translated into English, German, French and Italian.

'Queens Football' ('*El fútbol de Las Regias*') was first published in *SoHo* magazine in August 2007.

QUEENS FOOTBALL

Alberto Salcedo Ramos

Translated by Rosalind Harvey

Mauricio Álvarez, better known as "La Madison", takes a small mirror from his bag. As he combs his wispy bleached-blond hair, he says he realised he was gay aged seven, while reading a Superman comic.

"As soon as I saw Clark Kent, I just flipped," he says, spluttering with laughter.

With a look of mock astonishment on his face, John Jairo Murillo, nicknamed "La Ñaña", says this is the "gayest confession" he has heard in all his thirty-seven years.

"You're so gay," he exclaims, clapping his hands together, "you even want to shag men in cartoon strips!"

Madison laughs out loud, as do the other members of *Las Regias*: The Queens. They're getting changed in the stands of the Misael Pastrana Borrero stadium, in the town of Riofrío, eastern Colombia, an area best known for its plentiful production of sugar cane. Made up entirely of transvestites, the team was formed in 1992 with the aim of raising funds to help Cali homosexuals suffering from Aids or drug addiction. They raise money by playing exhibition matches in local neighbourhoods and nearby towns, and receive the odd donation too. But finding sufficient funds is getting increasingly difficult. They recently had to give up on the idea of competing at the Gay World Cup, held in Buenos Aires, because they failed to raise enough money to cover the cost of flights and a hotel.

This afternoon, as has become customary, the players gossip loudly while they change into their strip. The most foul-mouthed of all is La Ñaña, the team's founder. He says that when "La Valeria" was a little baby he used to sit on top of his bottle; that "La Britney" was born with a dummy up his ass; that "La Natalia" is as wet as water in a vase, "La Canasto" is a pansy in next door's yard, and "La Cuto" is so gay that when he sees a penis spray-painted on the ground, he rubs it out with his behind.

"And this one?" he says, referring to "La Iguana", who is doubled up with laughter. "If he'd spent another fifteen seconds in his mother's womb, he'd have been born with a pussy."

The stadium is small, with capacity for around a thousand spectators. The bare concrete stands are practically deserted. The game will kick off in an hour, by which time some five hundred people are expected to have shown up. The Las Regias players continue to preen themselves in a ritual that, for the moment, seems better suited to a beauty salon than a football pitch. There's still not a ball in sight, and instead an abundance of hair extensions, painted nails, dyed hair, lipsticks, plucked eyebrows and make-up.

"You know what, honey?" says La Ñaña. "Write down that the Las Regias players are all gay, but there are definitely no fags or fruits here, because fags are always doing favours for others, while fruits go rotten and get thrown at people."

Everyone bursts out laughing. Diego Fernando García, better known as "Melissa Williams", takes a little five-a-side ball from his bag and tells Óscar Gil, whose nickname is "La Natalia", to go in goal so that they can practise free kicks. For a moment it looks as if the first shot is going to end up in the back of the net, for instead of trying to punch the ball clear, La Natalia flaps his hands around at the side of his body, like a penguin trying to make sense of its useless wings. However, by chance, the ball bounces against his body and rolls away towards the touchline. La Natalia runs hysterically out of the goal, as if he's just made a World Cup-winning penalty save. Through their campness, these players transform football, a quintessentially macho sport, into a dance of turtle doves. If the spectators give them a standing ovation, it's not just out of politeness, but to reward them for having turned their very transvestism into the butt of the joke. Perhaps, deep down, those watching prefer having Las Regias caged in here, like circus freaks, to seeing them out and about in the streets, mixing with the rest of society. Watching them running jubilantly after the ball while the crowd claps and shouts brings to mind an old idea: man invented humour to comfort himself for being what he is.

Pedro Julio Pardo is a hot-tempered business administrator and co-ordinator of the Santamaría Foundation, which safeguards the rights of the LGBT population – lesbian, gay, bisexual and transgender people – in Cali, Colombia's third most important city. Pardo, who works closely with Las Regias, is of the opinion that, although it is discriminatory, transvestites have the right to band together to form their own football team, or to do any other activity for that matter. After all, are they really welcome in the stadiums where straight men play? "This country," he adds, "has left them with only two career options: prostitution and hairdressing. So building their own ghetto is a defence mechanism against discrimination."

"When we fags play football," he says, "we're making a statement about the lack of tolerance in society: if we're not allowed to play with the men, we'll form our own team."

Pardo sees the existence of Las Regias as an opportunity for Cali's transgender community to publicise its problems. Firstly, he cites the constant violence they endure. In just nine months, between November 2006 and August 2007, twelve transvestites were murdered and fifteen were shot or stabbed. Some have turned up naked on patches of waste ground, multiple signs of torture making plain the unremitting hatred of their assailants. At the weekends, groups of drunk young men leave clubs, carrying air guns, and practise their aim by firing at transsexuals' silicone breasts.

My chat with Pardo takes place in the Madison hair salon, located in the Siete de Agosto neighbourhood. It's a building on a corner, painted red and white. Inside, the walls bristle with mirrors and photographs of different hairstyles. There are also shelves with trophies and photos of Las Regias. There's a sense of obsessive cleanliness about the place: the make-up on the dressing table meticulously tidy, the furniture polished to a sheen, the smell of detergent. The salon is owned by Mauricio Álvarez – forty-two years old, five feet five – known in Cali's gay scene by his nickname, "La Madison". At the game yesterday, Álvarez came across as being excessively effeminate. Today, however, he's much more restrained. He wields his razor firmly and is even a little brusque when he reaches for his customer's head, a young man of around twenty.

At first Álvarez concentrates on his work and pays little attention to what Pardo is saying. But as he sweeps up the hair scattered over the floor, he joins in the conversation. In his opinion, transsexuals are the most marginalised group in the entire LGBT community.

"If it's hard for society to accept a run-of-the-mill gay," he says, "imagine how complicated things get when the gay dresses like a woman or gets himself some tits."

Neither straight men nor women consider the transsexual as being of their gender, but rather as someone in fancy dress, a caricature. Even conventional gay men reject transsexuals, considering them ludicrous creatures who have to put on a skirt to take on their sexuality. The police who patrol the city often move transsexuals on from the same public spaces where they're allowed to work as prostitutes. Where the harassment of the outside world ends – explains La Madison – the personal conflicts begin. Initially there's the chasm between what the transsexual wants to project to society and the perception people really have of him. What's more, being obliged to live trapped in a body he does not want weighs heavily on him: he suffers each night in his bedroom at the end of the day, retracing the steps of his own metamorphosis; then he must destroy the nocturnal butterfly he's created, and allow the old beetle to re-emerge. Removing make-up and rediscovering the blueish shadow of a beard hidden under the powder is a daily death only those who've experienced it can comprehend, according to La Madison. "Perhaps it's because of the depression these problems cause," he concludes, "that transsexuals are so prone to drug addiction."

Sometimes Álvarez gives the impression that he is more interested in talking to his own image reflected back in the mirror than in addressing Pardo. He goes back to being the man with the limp gestures he was during the game. You can tell a mile off that he's fond of his own image. Pardo suddenly points at a photo of Álvarez hanging on the wall, and asks where it was taken.

"A house in Alfonso López," Álvarez says, "when I was eighteen."

In the photo, Álvarez – his head tilted to the right, a languid look on his face – appears in a Roman tunic and sandals, with a laurel wreath on his head.

"I've got a really gay face there," he exclaims with a smile.

I ask him to describe what a "gay face" looks like, and he hesitates before giving me a metaphorical answer:

"It's a face that looks like a biscuit about to crumble."

The house, Álvarez adds, belonged to "La Leo", the oldest homosexual in south-east Cali. He died of Aids, shut up in his room so that no one could see him, because, as he told it, he didn't want to alarm all the pretty young boys who'd once been his lovers. The curious thing about the story is that La Leo made every boy he took to bed dress up as a Roman, then he took a picture of him. Thus he managed to put together a hefty photo album that became a hot topic of discussion in certain circles of the city. It was said that its pages featured pop stars, footballers and the sons of a number of notable politicians. Spiteful tongues claim the crowd that hung around his house when he was dying was motivated not by solidarity, but by the desperate need to find out what had happened to the photos. There are various different theories as to the album's whereabouts. The most popular claims it ended up in the hands of a drug trafficker, who used it to fuel a fire on the shores of the River Pance. With a smile Álvarez tells us that he swiped the photo of himself, the one we now see hanging on the wall, from La Leo's album years before it became an urban legend.

The conversation switches back to the difficulties inherent in transgender life. "A man who displays himself on the streets in a belly top and high heels," says Pardo, "is aware that his decision has a price, and he's prepared to pay it. He knows that, dressed like that, no one will offer him a job. He knows that he's making himself vulnerable to extremists capable of killing him. But by the time he's reached that point, there's no going back, and he doesn't want to in any case. He sets about his crusade knowing full well that it will be both self-affirming and suicidal. Many of these men fight tooth and nail for the tiny space fate has afforded them and, rather than sacrifice themselves, they become propagators of the very violence they denounce."

"The hostile environment makes them aggressive," he then adds.

It is also known that some of these men openly sell drugs on the street and become involved with minors.

Andrés Santamaría, an ombudsman in Valle del Cauca, is a twenty-eight-year-old lawyer. He operates from an office in a huge mansion with a pool, which was confiscated from a member of Cali's mafia by the Colombian government. Santamaría informs me that in Cali there are approximately three thousand transsexuals. Of these, three hundred work as prostitutes and the rest as hairdressers. In his opinion, removing people from the streets they control is not something that should be done by force, but rather it demands a social response. It's a job that's become too difficult in a city where, as he puts it, an unjust and discriminatory mindset has always prevailed. According to a study he himself conducted, poor people in Cali who commit minor offences are held, on average, for thirty-six hours, rich people for three.

"The region's economic development," he explains, "was due in part to the sugar mills, which prospered thanks to slavery. And this gave rise to the hegemonic mindset that still prevails today."

When the writer Gustavo Álvarez Gardeazábal launched his campaign to become governor of the region a few years ago, several leaders attempted to discredit him for being homosexual. The writer defended himself irritably, arguing that he would govern with his head, not with his ass.

Santamaría says that the fact that the rights of the LGBT community are now taken seriously has stoked up old bigoted attitudes. Some pundits see his initiatives not as a democratic duty, but as a symptom of immorality. A radio journalist recently accused him of "fagging up" the city. "This story," adds Santamaría, "reflects who we are as a country: on the surface we're talking about the problems faced by a particular group, but what we're really talking about is Colombia's age-old problem of intransigence, whereby anyone different is viewed as a transgressor and must be erased from the face of the earth. This is why we live through conflict after conflict."

Looking at the bigger picture, Santamaría attributes huge symbolic value to Las Regias. More than just helping transgender people who've fallen on hard times, they have brought to the foreground several important issues related to urban coexistence. Some of the nearly forty transvestites who make up his squad – such as "La Iguana" and "La Paulito" – have found in the team an opportunity to battle their drug addictions.

Las Regias make unlikely footballers: they are always falling over, they kick the ball up in the air when they're less than a foot from goal, they can't control the ball on their chests, never mind with their feet, and they're incapable of passing to a teammate a mere ten yards away. This clumsiness, which is not deliberate but natural, paradoxically becomes their most persuasive weapon. The spectators indulge them because they see them as actors in a parody. If people saw them performing headers like Miroslav Klose or dribbling like Ronaldinho, they wouldn't forgive them their painted nails and false eyelashes.

At half-time, Las Regias' opponents, a women's team from Riofrío, are 3-0 up. The almost 200 people who have come to the stadium are watching the choreographed show that Édinson Aramburu, another Las Regias player, is performing in the centre circle. The Las Regias team, meanwhile, are gathered in the same stands they got changed in earlier. Instead of anxiously discussing a strategy that might get them back on level terms, they're joking around again. As ever, the ringleader is La Ñaña – five feet six, green eyes, bleached-blond hair – who is giving the goalkeeper a hard time.

"Honey, you don't stop a thing, you're supposed to be a dam, not a dame."

Everyone bursts out laughing. I seize the opportunity to ask La Ñaña, in the same deadpan tone of voice he uses, why he mocks transgender people so much. Is he perhaps homophobic? I see a mischievous look in his eye, but he suddenly adopts a serious face.

"We take the insults society throws at us and we defuse them by making jokes of them."

However, his composure instantly evaporates.

"What are you going to say about me in this piece?" he asks, putting his hands on his hips and looking at me defiantly. As I stay silent, he has an idea.

"Put down that I'm not masculine, I'm *ass*-culine."

This time the one who laughs the hardest is La Valeria – thirty-seven years old, six feet tall, dark skin.

I ask La Ñaña to be serious for a minute so we can talk about football. What I've seen this afternoon – I say it dramatically – I find very worrying. If Las Regias were to represent Colombia at the Gay World Cup, they'd almost certainly be thrashed by Argentina, by Brazil, even by Guatemala – just think! His answer is a gem of black humour.

"Oh, sweetie, if they thrash the men's team, they're bound to give a bunch of fairies a good thrashing!"

This time I'm the one who bursts out laughing. Shortly afterwards, as I go back to my place to watch the second half, I wonder again about the spectators' motives for coming to watch Las Regias play. Perhaps they're trying to feel better about themselves by donating a few coins to help pay for the treatment of a gay man suffering from Aids or prostate cancer. Perhaps they're seeking an injection of surrealist humour from the players' sporting incompetence. Whatever the reason, I suspect they're not yet ready to accept the transvestites beyond the walls of this stadium.

Marco Avilés. Peru, 1978. Journalist and editor. He is content manager at Cometa, an initiative dedicated to telling stories in different settings and locations (cometa.pe). He has had one book published, *Día de visita* (Libros del KO, Spain), and he previously edited the *crónicas* magazine *Etiqueta Negra*. He lives in Lima with his girlfriend, two ginger cats and a hairless dog. His writing can be found and followed at www.marcoaviles.com.

'The Goal-Begetting Women of the Andes' ('*Las bombarderas de los Andes*') was first published in February 2007 in *Etiqueta Negra*.

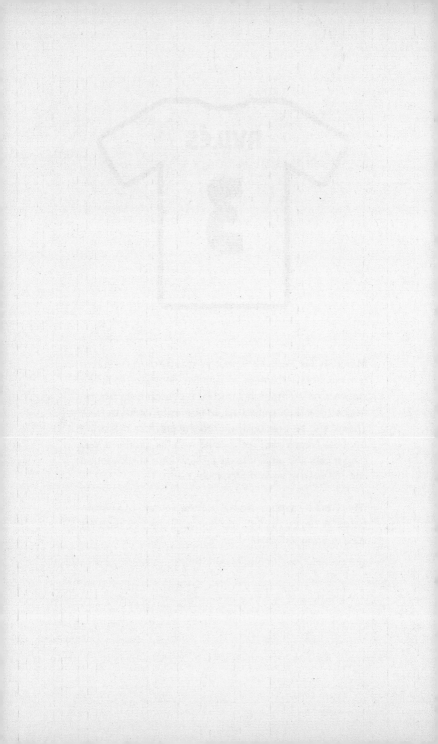

THE GOAL-BEGETTING WOMEN OF THE ANDES

Marco Avilés

Translated by Rachael McGill

Benedicta Mamani gets her football from the kitchen and limps out into an icy December morning. Yesterday she walked for miles through the mountains, herding sheep. Today, her legs are black and blue. At 4,000 metres above sea level, the Peruvian Andes are like a natural freezer, the chimneys of houses scattered about the summits condemned to never-ending toil. Benedicta Mamani can't read or write, but she knows heat relieves muscular pain. She sits down in a field and rubs her legs with plantain, an analgesic that grows in the back garden of her hut. Missing morning training is unthinkable.

Mamani is forty years old and Churubamba's star centre-forward. Churubamba is a village located five hours south of Cusco, with a population of 250 *campesinos*. Its women's football team has won the Andahuaylillas district championship five times running. The tiny outcrop of adobe buildings stands midway between the frozen mountains and the temperate Cusco Valley, site of the former Inca capital. It's six a.m. A megaphone connected to a car battery sends its alarm call echoing through the streets: "Attention, ladies! Oats have arrived! Assemble at the football pitch. A game will be played afterwards." Benedicta Mamani gets to her feet. She goes back into her kitchen, grabs a handful of coca leaves. Desperate, she stuffs them in her mouth like sweeties. If living at this altitude is an extreme sport, coca is its performance-enhancing drug, easing pain, suppressing hunger, banishing cold. When the effect kicks in, Mamani will be ready to play. For the last time.

Churubamba means "snail" in Quechua, the language spoken by over 3 million people in the Peruvian Andes. The most common second language at this high and erratic altitude could be said to be football. The landscape is a natural imitation of a huge stadium: terraced mountains enclosing a green plain. There is no police station, no church – not even a cross – but there are two wooden goals, hammered in at either end of the large town-square-cum-marketplace-cum-football-pitch. About sixty mud houses with thatched roofs nestle around the square, along with a school, where reading and counting in Quechua are taught. Football, the universal language of leisure, has reached Churubamba ahead of Spanish, books and medicine. There are still parts of the world where capitalism can tout old novelties. If the earth weren't round, Churubamba would gaze directly at the other highest, most isolated settlements on the planet: Wenchuan in China, Potosí in Bolivia, Lhasa in Tibet. But our world is a football. In the universe of the high mountains, where public transport and shoes barely exist, Churubamba's champion women's team are perhaps the female equivalent of the Brazilian national side.

Benedicta Mamani's calves are covered in bruises above her *ojotas*, sandals made from the coarse rubber of used car tyres. Limping, she finally reaches the football pitch, the Churubamba market square. Like all the village women, she wears a dress she made herself, with four layers of coloured skirts. She also wears a white blouse, an alpaca wool jacket, and a square, broad-brimmed hat decorated with coloured embroidery and sequins. This is their official football kit, not to entice the world's photographers, on the prowl for exotic images, but because it's what they wear every day, to do everything. On the outskirts of the Bolivian capital, La Paz, there's a village called Cattuyo. Here footballing *campesinas* play to the crowds: along with their traditional full skirts, they wear boots and professional team shirts, a sort of official uniform for the cameras. But what stands out as being most exotic are the tourists themselves, with their digital cameras, indiscreet questions and hunger for the quirky and quaint.

Every fortnight, the municipality of the district of Andahuaylillas sends a truck full of oats to Churubamba. To get there, the vehicle has to negotiate high precipices on a road muddied by rain. Its average speed is ten miles per hour. Churubamba itself produces only potatoes, corn and a few other vegetables, like carrots and tomatoes. The day the grain arrives is akin to a public holiday: the town comes to a standstill. The men leave their sowing to carry the sacks, the women gather in the square/pitch to divide up the food according to the number of people in each household. In Churubamba, the square is the centre of the universe. When you leave your house, you end up in the square. When you leave the square, you're back at your house. After the oats have been distributed, the women always do two things: have a community meeting, play football. The novelty of soccer was discovered a generation ago. The women are better players than the men, if being better means taking home trophies from five consecutive tournaments, played against the six other women's teams in the Andahuaylillas district. The Churubamba women have earned a loyal fan base, the right to use the football pitch, and much applause. Every game in the village is treated as training to keep them in good shape to compete against their neighbours. In a few days, Andahuaylillas will host its annual festivities, which include a women's football exhibition match with a trophy to play for, courtesy of the mayor. The men of the village, who've never won their tournament, watch from the stands, proud supporters, happily resigned to being over-shadowed by their wives.

This particular morning, there's also a tribunal in the village: a woman is accused of consuming too many oats. Her name is Toribia Ccopa. She's obese. She kneels at the centre of a human circle on one side of the square. The judgment, like all decisions here, will be communal. When you marry, the community gives you a piece of land. When you die, the land returns to the community. If you steal, the community takes you to the Vilcanota River and whips you while you think about what you've done. If you're found to have a lover, you're expelled from the town. The assembly contains twenty women and no more than ten men. Someone makes the accusation. It's Benedicta Mamani.

"Why are you eating so much?" she says in Quechua. "You should leave it for the poor."

Ccopa, the accused, remains silent, bowing her head in shame, wounded by the laughter of the small crowd around her.

"Ridicule can be a terrible punishment in a village of sixty families," Martín Pilco explains later. He's Churubamba's schoolteacher, the only adult who speaks Spanish.

"This woman will have to put up with the teasing for a while, then show she's willing to change."

The accused woman retreats, mournful, to the far end of the square, towards one of the corner spots. Her fate is that of all players punished for bad behaviour: the red card.

According to FIFA, there are 40 million women worldwide playing organised football as part of clubs or associations. If that number were represented as an area on a globe, it would cover no more than two or three countries in Europe, the continent with the most women footballers. But FIFA is unaware of Churubamba, and Benedicta Mamani is unaware of FIFA's statistics. She can't read. While the men remove the last sacks of grain from the square, she and eight other women form their team. They stand round the ball, discussing their captain's injuries. The ground is covered in the same scrubby grass as the rest of the mountainside. Puddles and patches of mud attest to last night's rains.

Pilco, the teacher, translates, as the centre-forward explains: "When I was a girl, no one, male or female, played football in Churubamba."

The story began in 1982, the year of the World Cup in Spain. In the first round Peru drew with Italy, one of the tournament favourites. But football mania had taken hold of the entire country months before. The government had declared public holidays for Peruvians to celebrate the results of the warm-up games: Peru 1 France 0 – in the Parc des Princes; Peru 2 Hungary 1. Peru still occasionally used to win football matches back then. The inhabitants of Churubamba listened on battery-operated radios, some went down the mountain to sneak looks at TV sets in neighbouring villages. Returning home, they gazed at the grass of their marketplace, with the eyes of a striker hungry for goals. The wooden posts and crossbars were erected with the help of priests from the Andahuaylillas church, who saw football as a possible remedy for Churubamba's social ills. These included alcoholism, an accessible vice that dated back to the times of the *haciendas*. Peruvian landowners were untitled feudal lords who could pay their workers with anything they liked, alcohol included. When agricultural reforms came, the land was divided up and the peasants acquired property: capitalism was arriving. Football came too. Benedicta Mamani was a girl then. She remembers her grandmother, already elderly, learning to kick a ball around. She drank less by the time she died. Later, during the 1990s, under the auspices of reducing rural poverty, Alberto Fujimori, the then president, backed a campaign of forced sterilisation of women. The plan reached Churubamba. Pilco tells of women going to the hospital in Andahuaylillas with stomach-aches and going home having had their tubes tied or an IUD inserted. At other times, medics toured the remote villages performing operations on the spot. As a result, for that decade, rural people remained poor, but fewer new poor people were born.

"We had to close the school. There were no pupils," the teacher remembers.

It's not hard to imagine the cruel impact of forced sterilisation on a community in which the women's role is to have children, the children's role to work the land. The women suddenly had in abundance the one thing all games need: free time. According to the teacher, they began to play simply because they unexpectedly had the leisure to do so. But it's hard to know whether this is quite true, to separate fact from fiction. The hospitals in the nearest cities kept no statistics on Fujimori's forced sterilisation campaign. The Peruvian human-rights ombudsman, La Defensoría del Pueblo, says 150,000 women were sterilised, but those figures are for the whole of Peru. Not all of them became football players, but then nor did they all live in a village like Churubamba, where life revolved around a football field. We know one thing: in 1999 the Catholic church in the area organised a sports tournament for all the rural mountain villages and municipalities of the town of Andahuaylillas. "We saw sport as a way of building bridges with isolated populations," says the town's parish priest. It was proposed that the men compete at football, their wives at volleyball. The women replied saying they knew how to kick a ball, too, and a category for women's football was created. The Churubamba women's team was victorious. So began their unstoppable ascent.

The referee's whistle sounds, ordering children and dogs to clear the marketplace. A mud wall separates the football pitch from the rest of Churubamba. Encarnacíon Taype, Benedicta Mamani's husband, sits on this wall, talking with a few other men. Taype wears jute trousers, a thin shirt and a *chullo*, the Andean conical wool bonnet, with flaps to protect his ears from the cold.

"Does he mind that his wife plays football? How much freedom do the women here have?"

"They have their duties as mothers, as we have ours as fathers," he says. "When those are done, everyone can play." Households in the mountains are generally matriarchal, the teacher explains. The women cook, care for the children, administer the finances. "A man can't sell a sheep without his wife's authorisation." Do the men hit the women? Yes. What do the women do about it? Hit back. "Or they can complain to the communal assembly, but then the man's punishment will be harsher," says Encarnacíon Taype. He makes himself comfortable in the stands. Women never play against men. Two teams come onto the pitch: nine players on each side, in flowered skirts and *ojotas*. The game is about to begin.

The first team is Mirador de Churubamba, its captain Benedicta Mamani. The other is Club Churubamba, led by Andrea Puma, a plump-cheeked woman of around twenty. She's Churubamba's top player, captain of the official village team since 2000.

"The losers can go back to cleaning up after their husbands," Andrea Puma jokes, hands on hips.

Another whistle from the referee. The ball flies off the pitch and a child lets out a wail from the stands. His mother abandons her midfield position to console him. Throw-in. Andrea Puma calls for the ball in the opposition box. She latches on to the ball, controls it in among her skirts, holds off a defender, plays a nutmeg through another's legs and skirts, shoots over the bar, into a cloud-patterned sky. Goal kick. The high ball creates confusion: at 4,000 metres, in a game involving players who are also mothers and heads of families, tactical discipline is somewhat lacking. Every woman abandons her position, chasing the ball. Benedicta Mamani, back in her own area, brings the ball down on her chest, traps it with her foot and punts it forward, in search of a teammate. She's focused on the game and no longer notices her purple, bruised calves. A striker tries a diving header, but fails to get on the end of it and lands with her stout legs splaying out beneath her skirts. Goal kick. A few minutes later, after another long punt forward, Benedicta Mamani cries out in pain: her big toe nail is bleeding, split in two. Her *ojotas* are great for walking on muddy earth, but terrible for performing toe-pokes. Benedicta Mamani leaves the field, supported by two colleagues. Without their captain, Mirador de Churubamba struggle through the rest of the match, neither side distinguishing itself. The game ends in a 0-0 draw. Stats: ten shots on target, three against the post, four over the bar. One of those four caused a slight delay as it struck the door of the school and bounced off past the stands and down the mountainside. It took ten minutes to get the ball back. The referee decides there'll be penalties. He's a thickset man of few words. The coloured woollen *chullo* on his head offsets his severity. "There has to be a winning team," he says. Final result: Mirador nil, Andrea Puma's Club Churubamba two. The prize for the winners is bread and cheese, with oranges for dessert, courtesy of the mayor of Andahuaylillas. The losing team gets the same. Everything in the town is communal, prizes and the thrill of competition included. When the adults get together for municipal duties, like cleaning the street, they divide into two teams, split the work in half, see who finishes first. There's no prize or punishment: the competition just means the job gets done quicker.

To celebrate the town's anniversary, the council in Andahuaylillas has organised an exhibition match between Churubamba and its own team, made up of a group of artisan craftswomen. These women went to school, speak Spanish, wear trainers. They also watch television and drink Coca-Cola. If they have an injury, they go to the chemist, buy a painkiller. They live globalisation, shop in its supermarket of well-being.

"They're nothing to fear," says Andrea Puma.

Benedicta Mamani lies on the ground on one side of the square. Andrea Puma offers her fizzy water.

"Women here are good at cooking, at looking after children, at helping the men with the harvest. We're strong. So we're good at football too."

The changing room of a women's football match in the Andes is like any changing room anywhere: a cauldron of infectious excitement. Courage, catharsis, faith. But if football is an ever-evolving version of warfare, a battle between eleven pairs of *ojotas* and eleven pairs of trainers might be expected to go the same way as one between an army equipped with bows and arrows and another with guided missiles. Is football a microscope through which to examine social differences? Is it the sport that best allows us to understand our world? Is the game capable of bridging the extremes of human experience, ironing out disparities and turning them into goal tallies? Attempting any such evaluation is like trying to predict the score of a game you've yet to watch. It will just be a game. Eleven skirts against eleven skirts.

On the day of the big skirts-versus-skirts match, the Andahuaylillas sky dawns clear and blue, an immense, hand-painted dome. The town's streets are tiny cobbled alleyways. A handful of tourists prowl around, taking photos: children kicking stones on their way to school, a woman with long plaits giving out milk, *campesinos* walking behind an indifferent cow. The houses have white walls, wooden balconies, brown tiled roofs. They surround a spacious square with four leafy trees, each as old as the church, built in 1650. The temple of Andahuaylillas is already open, the large front door, with its many knockers, the mouth of a monster in repose. Travel books call it "Peru's Sistine Chapel". Inside, tourists gape at the terrifying murals. The guides tell them the figure of the devil played an important role when the Catholic missionaries came here with the Spanish *conquistadores*. Idolatry had to be eradicated, the Inca cult of the Sun supplanted by fear of God. While civilisation reached the city, the indigenous mountain communities carried on as before. And still do today.

"The religious struggle continues," says Luis Herrera, a Jesuit priest in jeans and shirtsleeves, as rosy-cheeked as an apostle in a painting of the Last Supper. His office is a table, a computer and a window overlooking the square. Behind it, the mountains tower, giants playing with the clouds. Hard to imagine that up at the summit is a village of women footballers.

Herrera sits on an old sofa. "The Brazilian Protestant and Evangelical Churches did their own evangelising here," he says. "They converted lots of communities. But we're the ones who introduced football." Herrera is the head of the Church of the Company of Jesus, but he's no fan of propaganda. In the 1980s, he remembers, alcoholism was one of the biggest problems in the rural communities of Cusco. Men and women drank every day. Violence was endemic, children were neglected, mortality from cirrhosis of the liver was high. Football, says Herrera, was a way of combating this negative behaviour. In some African countries, football is used to stop men making war. In Sierra Leone, Benin and Angola, NGOs employ European coaches to bring sport to people displaced by civil war. If the business of football is an ever-expanding religion, as Manuel Vázquez Montalbán has said, its missionaries have been as unwitting and anonymous as those of Cusco. At the end of the nineteenth century, British and Portuguese merchant seamen brought footballs to Brazil. They played on the beaches, and the curiosity of the locals was aroused: the story of a great footballing nation had begun. In Churubamba, where there are no books or televisions, the priests became apostles for the prophet of sport. Perhaps that's how globalisation works in football: FIFA, a lazy Vatican, hopes that by 2010 as many women as men will be playing professional football. The world continues to offer virgin territories, isolated but not unconquerable:

football today is civilisation's fastest-growing cultural industry. The business of colonising feet.

"FIFA knows nothing about geography," says the priest. "What we hope football can achieve here is the integration of two worlds: the city and the mountain villages. That's something that hasn't happened in five hundred years."

Father Hererra has goals of his own, though if the full-time whistle were to blow right now, he'd be in arrears. After working for several decades in Churubamba, he says with resignation, the Church had to abandon the community because of its inaccessibility and the lack of money for missionary work. Some Protestant sects, the evangelical ones in particular, stepped into the gap. Now, nearly all of the area has renounced Catholicism. It's a match in which the priests have lost possession of the ball. Hererra won't be going to watch the Andahuaylillas women take on their visitors from Churubamba. He has work to do. That very evening, functionaries will arrive from Lima, the distant capital, to inaugurate the Sistine Chapel's new lighting system. Even this church relies on tourism to survive. Outside the office, the sky darkens over empty streets. It's about to rain again.

Black clouds cast their shadows over a stadium that could hold 5,000 people, if there were more fans of women's football in town. Today there are no more than 200 curious onlookers. The cement stands are painted the colours of the rainbow. In the Seventies, a lawyer from Cusco claimed that these were the colours of the flag of the Inca Empire. The fabrication became a truth, touted to tourists. In the centre of the main stand, the mayor of Andahuaylillas eyes the clouds with concern. If it rains, he says, the match will have to be called off. The prize, a team strip, will be divided among all the players. He is Guillermo Chillihuane, born in a nearby village. As a child, he was sent to school in the city. He learnt Spanish, did odd jobs, saved up to study engineering at university in Cusco. Many in Churubamba, as in other Quechua villages, dream of something similar for their children. They send them to school in the city, but because it's too far to get back to the village in the same day, the parents have built a settlement of mud houses at the foot of the mountains, next to a river. New Churubamba is a ghost town. The children live there from Monday to Friday, sleeping on sheepskins, sheltering from the cold.

"Because they're not with their families, they wander the city, begging from tourists," Chillihuane says. "Sport is a way of tackling the problem. That's why we're building more football pitches."

To enjoy the comforts of living at the foot of the mountains, people from Churubamba would have to pay a high admission price: they'd have to learn Spanish and have disposable income. Most people don't meet the criteria. They continue to regard modernity – television, hospitals, university – as a spectacle that happens elsewhere. When they come down the mountain to play football, they're like aliens from another planet, one that plays football in secret. They play, and leave.

Churubamba are 1-0 up with fifteen minutes to play. Andrea Puma glares at the opposition goal, hands on skirts, cursing her aim having just shot over the bar. Goal kick. The ball travels fifty yards, threatening the away team's goal. The *ojotas* defend, trying to deal with the danger, but the trainers attack, pouncing as if in an ambush. The long, wet grass is causing trouble for the visiting team. Guillermina Gutiérrez, a defender with plaits so long they disappear beneath the waistband of her skirt, gets on the ball. She plans to clear it downfield but, with all her weight on one leg, she slips and ends up flat on her back, counting clouds. "Foul!" cries the crowd of children and husbands. The referee waves play on.

The mayor looks at his watch, gets up from his seat in the stand and comes down to talk to the referee. Out on the pitch, the Andahuaylillas players are anxious to know how long they've got left to equalise. Their kit is a crimson skirt, white tights, white blouse, white trainers. The Churubamba players – brown skirts, red sweaters, *ojotas* – are exhausted. There's no closing down as the home side fires in a shot from just outside the area. Two of the visiting team have gone off injured with broken toenails. Those still standing fend the old enemy off with some fairly tasty tackling. It's all over. The winning team set off like sprinters in a race, rushing to the sideline, as if fleeing from the prizes. They collect their babies, lifting them straight to their breasts. In their corner, the losing team massage their wounds. Question: why did you lose?

"The Churubamba women are stronger. They're not afraid of a ball in the face or a kick in the shins. But they have very little technical skill."

In the other camp, the answer is the universal cliché:

"We were the better team."

The injured Benedicta Mamani congratulates her teammates, hands them glasses of fizzy water. Her eleven-year-old daughter, Renata Taype, is with her.

"She's a good little player," her mother says, patting the child on the head. "But she's going to carry on studying."

Unlike her mother, Renata Taype wears shoes, white plimsolls. Thin brown toes poke out from a hole at the front of one of them. She can speak Spanish. When she grows up, she wants to be a teacher in the school in the city, and live in a house with a television.

"I'll live there with my parents," she says, then breaks into a run behind her mother. It's started raining.

The raindrops are like tiny balls aimed at people's heads. The prize-giving ceremony is swift. The mayor distributes synthetic football shirts, numbered 1 to 22, to the winners. They pull them on over their red sweaters. Now they're a professional team. More rain falls on the roofless stadium. In a matter of minutes the show is declared over. The mayor of Andahuaylillas climbs into a minibus with his town's team. The Churubamba players, their children and husbands, climb into a truck covered with a coarse tarpaulin. The return drive to the village will be perilous and take over three hours. Next time they play, perhaps the Churubamba women's team will wear the shirts they've just won. Will this be the kit that unites the mountains and the city? Why not give them trainers? The mayor's answer opens a tunnel in time: "Because their feet are so broad, they won't fit into anything other than their *ojotas*." He speaks from the comfort of the minibus, but before he goes he tells me why it's always better to work with children than with adults: because the spread of civilisation is a slow process, achieved one step at a time, starting with the feet.

Álex Ayala Ugarte is a Spaniard by birth, a Bolivian by heart and a stutterer by vocation. He was the Sunday editor of the Bolivian newspaper *La Razón*, the creative non-fiction editor of the weekly *Pulso* and founder of *Pie Izquierdo*, the first non-fiction magazine in Bolivia. He contributes to publications such as *Etiqueta Negra*, *Paula*, *Virginia Quarterly Review*, *Séptimo Sentido*, *Frontera D* and *Internazionale*. He has taken part in *crónica* workshops alongside journalists such as Alberto Salcedo, Francisco Goldman, Jon Lee Anderson and Alma Guillermoprieto. He won the National Journalism Prize in Bolivia in 2008. He contributed to the anthology of Bolivian *crónicas*, *Bolivia a toda costa: Crónicas de un país de ficción*, and his first book, *Los mercaderes del Che*, was recently published in Bolivia and Spain.

'Football's Strangest Kidnapping' ('*El secuestro más extraño del fútbol*') was first published in the Bolivian magazine *El Día D* and subsequently published in the magazines *Sole* (Colombia), *Emeequis* (Mexico), *SoHo* (Argentinian edition), *Séptimo Sentido* (El Salvador) and in *Los Mercaderes del Che* (Libros del K.O, Spain).

FOOTBALL'S STRANGEST KIDNAPPING

Álex Ayala Ugarte

Translated by Chris Lloyd

When Yuri Villarroel scored for La Paz Fútbol Club on January 23, he had no idea that in a few weeks' time he'd be kidnapped. It was a bizarre goal: it glanced in off his thigh. And it was a historic goal: his first as a professional, and the first Bolivian league goal scored in an official match played in the city of El Alto, at the Los Andes stadium, which is one of the highest on the planet at 4,080 metres above sea level. At that altitude, in other parts of the world they don't have cities, they have mountains. At that altitude, in countries like Switzerland, they build ski slopes. Yuri, though, scored his momentous goal without any fuss, calm as a lawyer putting his seal on a contract.

He scored in the twenty-sixth minute of the second half, having come off the bench; following a foul on the left wing and a free kick, a free kick drilled in like a space rocket by Argentinian Alejandro Molina, a space rocket destined never to return to earth, for it struck Yuri's leg and he steered it past the keeper, steered it on the volley, into the back of the net. All in the blink of an eye: now you see it, now you don't. After that: silence, the stands erupting, Yuri running to the touchline, a cry on his lips, no shirt on his back. Right there. High as the sky. Looking at bank upon bank of fans. Feeling on fire, immune to the ten-degree temperature.

One month later, the same place, the same setting, and Yuri does feel the cold. It's eight o'clock at night and inside the ground, in the changing rooms, the coffee they've put on to boil isn't enough to keep them warm. Inside, white soulless walls. Inside, the plastic chairs the players use to get changed on are huddled closer together than usual. Inside, they check their watches every five minutes. Inside, some talk on their phones, others nap. Inside, the hostages, the entire La Paz Fútbol Club first-team squad: the players, the coach, the doctor, the physio, the coach driver who brought them there. Inside is better than outside. Outside looks like the end of the world.

Outside, sand and wind: the north wind that overwhelms the streets, turns them into a storm drain. Outside, houses that all look the same: all of them clones, all of them adobe, bare brick and corrugated iron. Outside, Cosmos 79: the never-ending neighbourhood, vast as a steppe, ruddy, tough, expressionless. Outside, the local people. The local people who heard on the radio that morning that their stadium would be shut down for being unsafe, the local people who mobilised themselves, the local people who padlocked the ground, the local people who said, "No one goes in, no one goes out." Outside, horizon, distance, oblivion. At over 4,000 metres: oblivion. Outside, the fans: the fans who kidnapped their own team.

Only the most desperate of fans would kidnap their own team. In Cosmos 79, those desperate fans were some 100 local people. It was a silent kidnapping, amicable even. No weapons. No preparations. A masterly checkmate in just one move: they simply sealed the doors, one by one, and waited for La Paz FC to finish training.

It really was parking the bus. Brilliant. Improvised. The only possible way for a place that doesn't appear in guidebooks or on tourist maps to cease being invisible for a moment or two.

"It wasn't a real kidnapping. It was purely tactical. How else could we put pressure on them not to close our ground?" asks Roberto Condori Chura, vice-president of the Cosmos 79 Central Council of Residents' Associations.

Roberto says that after an inspection and several renovations, the Los Andes stadium was authorised at the start of the year, by the league, to host official matches. It was local people, brimming with enthusiasm, who'd repaired the showers, filled in the holes and enclosed the facilities with security fencing.

"We did everything they asked of us. There were even women working pick in hand. That's why no one can understand why they now want to ban us from using the stadium. They reckon we can't ensure safety; that people shouldn't enter our stands. But no one's died here. Friend and foe are welcome alike."

Roberto is holding a brown leather diary in his left hand, in which he makes a note of everything that happens in the neighbourhood: the complaints, the claims, the problems, the incidents. Absolutely everything. He wears a black mac, highly polished shoes, white shirt and dark sunglasses. He isn't one, but he has the hard face of a civil servant. And a clear idea: no one has the right to deprive El Alto of top-flight football.

"No league, no matches," he hisses. And he points to some youngsters playing a school match in the stadium, moving slightly clumsily, running after the ball like it was an elusive hare. "We won't allow it!" he exclaims, with genuine disgust. "They're discriminating against us: these kids should be able to see the players they admire so much, playing here, where they were born."

In Cosmos 79, like in the *favelas* of Rio and the *villas* of Buenos

Aires, football has become an escape valve. The kids here want to be like Cristiano Ronaldo or Lionel Messi, the latest rock stars in the annals of football. And the fact that a star like Messi signed his first contract on a serviette gives them hope: his story is that of a humble kid who was able to conquer the world thanks to his skills on the football pitch. He shows them that they too can triumph: Messi, who stands just five feet five, often scores goals against six-foot giants. Perhaps that's why Mexican writer and journalist Juan Villoro says "there's not a defence or keeper that can stop him".

But on the day of the kidnap a handful of padlocks stopped a whole team. Only a couple of youth players got away. "They jumped over a ten-foot wall," Carlos Eulate, one of the groundsmen, told me some weeks later. When someone came into the changing room and told them they were locked in, the rest of the squad thought it was a joke. Many only really took it seriously when the team doctor, Cristian Guevara, started handing out vitamin A and C pills, so they didn't catch a chill.

Journalist Ricardo Bajo says that La Paz FC is "an atypical club, almost unique in the world". They have few fans, barely any junior teams and they train on rented pitches. Ricardo says "it's really just one man's team": Mauricio González's, who over the years has transferred players to such exotic locations as Azerbaijan and China. Ricardo also tells me that González was the president of Yacimientos Petrolíferos Fiscales Bolivianos, the state-owned oil company, and that one day he wanted to buy a football club, so he simply went shopping and "bought himself one".

It's a Thursday in late March and I'm in front of a house that looks like an office, outside a door with no nameplate, identified by nothing more than the number 504. Between the door and the house is a courtyard with a palm tree, a gardener and a rather improvised-looking personal gym. Inside, in the room where Mauricio González is waiting for me, there's hardly any furniture: just a trophy or two, some photos and a wooden table at which he's securely seated in a chair. Without looking up, while checking something on his laptop, he tells me he can give me twenty minutes. "I'm a very busy man," he says.

Mauricio is a middle-aged guy, tall, stocky, well dressed – a suit with a check jacket and an elegant handkerchief in the breast pocket – who like most of his business friends, is constantly checking his mobile phone.

Using his mobile, Mauricio controls the little world that surrounds him: he gives orders, he negotiates new signings or transfers, he offers exclusives to journalists, and from time to time he talks to the coaching staff, because although it's hard to admit, his team, the team that kicks a ball about on top of the world (at 4,000 metres), is kicking its heels at the bottom of the table.

But his mobile wasn't much good to him the day they locked his team in the Los Andes stadium. That day he had to go to El Alto and negotiate in person.

"So that the residents would release the hostages?" I ask him.

"No. God, no. It wasn't a kidnapping."

Mauricio González is now telling me his team wasn't kidnapped.

"But they wouldn't let the players out," I say. "They held them inside the ground."

"No, no, of course they didn't," he insists. "My players weren't held." He thinks a bit, as though he's doubting himself. And then he emphasises the end of the sentence: "They weren't *held*," he stresses.

He does it, I think, so that I won't have any doubt.

Then Mauricio says it was all mutually agreed, that they took the players sandwiches and roast chicken to stop them from feeling hungry. That they let them go by ten o'clock at night so they wouldn't fall ill.

"They let them go," I repeat.

"They let them go," he repeats.

They let them go after everyone had calmed down. They let them go after no one paid a blind bit of notice to the local people.

La Paz Fútbol Club used to be named Atlético González, after Mauricio's father. They had their glory days: in 2007 they won the Copa Aerosur, and they once finished second in the league. But for the last few years they've languished at the foot of the table.

"Not so long ago we were the third team in La Paz. What we needed was to find a home where we'd be loved, because the people of La Paz are very loving, but they have a problem: they're either fans of The Strongest or Bolívar," Mauricio said with a smile. "For me, the trade-off with the *alteños* is excellent: we gain a fan base and they get to have football in their own home, their own stadium. That's why we wanted to play in El Alto."

Some years ago, faced with the absence of an organised supporters' club, Mauricio looked into getting a company from the Colorados infantry regiment to rouse the fans with their drums and smart uniforms. He wanted a wow factor: the Colorados are usually tall, handsome lads, eye-catching in their extravagant outfits, like toy soldiers. They form part of the presidential guard. And indeed they guard the Government Palace. What better way to win over the terraces?

But what seemed like a winning formula soon fizzled out. And so, for now, La Paz Fútbol Club remains something of a spare part, and El Alto still lacks the vital organ of its own football team. The dream won't properly be complete until next season, when the claret and blues change their name and officially become El Alto Fútbol Club: El Alto's football club.

It's Sunday in Cosmos 79. Right by the entrance to the Los Latinos restaurant is a table football: The Strongest versus Bolívar. The

56

wooden footballers – one side tiger-striped, the other sky blue – are pale from so much use. They've doubtless taken part in some epic encounters.

"So when are you going to paint one of the teams claret and blue?" I ask Olimpia Mamani, about thirty-five years old and owner of the restaurant. "They're the La Paz FC colours, aren't they? Don't they represent El Alto now?"

Olimpia rewards me with a half smile. Then she shrugs. She doesn't know when yet. There are still a lot of *bolívaristas* and *estronguistas* in the neighbourhood.

When The Strongest came up to El Alto to play against La Paz FC, the Los Latinos restaurant was full to bursting. The first floor – the main floor, the one with the dining tables, the one painted cream that serves local food and plays *cumbia* and *chicha* music – was packed with diners. But so was the second floor, the third floor and the fourth floor – the ones still being built.

"They cleared me out of sodas. Out of sweets. Out of cigarettes. Out of food. Out of beer. They cleared out my whole storeroom," Olimpia tells me.

The whole building became a sort of improvised stand, the people's terrace, where you could watch the game for just a few pesos. Upstairs there were people standing up, others sitting on plastic chairs: children, men and women. In the middle of a construction site, in the middle of piles of bricks.

Outside Los Latinos, there were people on tops of lorries, microbuses and all sorts of other vehicles. Many wearing multicoloured scarves, in support of one side or the other, under a typical Altiplano sun, a sun that burns but doesn't warm.

From time to time forty-eight-year-old Gladys Ticona sells *empanadas tucumanas* outside the Cosmos 79 market, a busy shed filled with trestles and blue nylon canopies that offer pasta, meat, fruit and vegetables. Today is Saturday, there's plenty of hustle and bustle, and she's protecting herself from the bright sunlight with a hat. She's also wearing a sky-blue uniform, visible from some way off. And she's manoeuvring a trolley with pots of *maní* groundnut sauce and *llajua* chilli sauce, for her customers to put on their *tucumanas*.

Gladys says there are a lot of street-food sellers in the neighbour-hood now (around 180). That stall plots have gone up in price since they built the stadium. That on match days, the real business round here isn't goals, it's food.

"When La Paz Fútbol Club play," she reckons, "some of us sell in a day what we wouldn't clear in a week."

Sounds perfect. Except that so far, and especially after the latest complaints about the ground – that the capacity is too small, that the safety barriers are too weak, that there's too much aggregate material, that media facilities are lacking, and so on and so forth – first division games have been few and far between.

That's why the tide hasn't turned for the better here yet. That's why Gladys says they protested.

"We've got nothing against the players. They're like sons to me. But what the league's doing to us is an injustice. And we won't put up with things like that round here. We react."

Gladys avoids calling what happened a few weeks ago a kidnap-ping. An "incident" she calls it. "There's no need to exaggerate what happened. It was nothing more than that: an incident."

As far as she's concerned, the exact word for it is "incident".

"And," she clarifies, "by ten o'clock we let all the players out through one of the back gates. But we didn't tell the journalists that, so they'd stay."

Kidnappings, like blind dates, have unforeseeable outcomes. In 1942, during the German occupation, the Dynamo Kiev players, held captive in their own city, chose to give up their lives rather than lose at their own ground to Hitler's team. "If you win, we will kill you," they were told; and that's what happened: they won, and were tortured and shot (some still wearing their kit). In Mexico, Peruvian player Reimond Manco, of Atlante, had better luck recently when he came through a kidnap unscathed. Because there never was a kidnapping: he'd made the whole thing up to avoid having to admit that he'd turned up for training late because he was drunk. Here, in Cosmos 79, the aim was simply to make the news: to appear in the media.

And this they did: at long last the neighbourhood made the news.

Meanwhile, in the changing rooms, the players faded into the background, out of the spotlight, resigned. For people used to camera flashes, microphones and being the centre of attention, nearly eight hours locked up must have been terribly dull.

They played cards. They listened to music on their phones or their iPods. They played jokes on each other. They struggled to get comfortable, propping their legs up or lying on stretchers. And they organised delegations of two or three to go to the main gate to find out how the negotiations were going. But the negotiations weren't going. Mauricio Méndez, the league chairman, wasn't answering their calls. Like someone switching off a light, he switched off his mobile phone and washed his hands of the matter.

When the temperature dropped, the ground became a fridge, and keeping limbs warm became increasingly difficult. There were no blankets. The physio worked overtime, moving from one leg to the next.

"But we understood the people perfectly," says Richard Rojas, a thirty-six-year-old defensive midfielder. "They're tremendously big-hearted people and they love their football. They protested because they wanted us here, in El Alto. Probably, if they hadn't done what they did, no one would have paid them any notice."

Like many other parts of El Alto, Cosmos 79 was once a ranch. It was known as Collpani and began to be developed in 1979, by Benigno Gómez, a man nicknamed "The Land Trader". It seems Benigno acted as agent for twenty-five tenant farmers who couldn't read or write, and whose land he soon sold.

Twenty years ago, there was no electricity here. Water came from wells, and the lucky few who had TVs ran them on batteries they got charged in another neighbourhood. In those days, football matches were still rather exotic. They played for a cow, or a bull. Sometimes for a llama.

These days there are buildings everywhere in El Alto and football pitches are improvised on every corner. Football here is almost a religion, practically the only thing that competes with the Evangelical Church and the sixty-plus Renaissance-style bell-towers the German priest Sebastián Obermaier had built, so that they're the first thing you notice from the plane as you land. Which is why it should come as no surprise to learn that the two structures that have put Cosmos 79 on the map are Obermaier's cathedral and the Los Andes stadium.

The cathedral stands on an old country cemetery next to the market and is both the leading spiritual centre in the area and a meeting place. For its part, the stadium is a bit of a white elephant. But according to the *alteño* writer Marco Alberto Quispe Villca, it's also one of the main reasons Cosmos 79 ceased being considered an El Alto backwater.

Soon the stands will be built and Los Andes will be able to house nearly 20,000 spectators, that's to say nearly half the neighbourhood's population, a neighbourhood with an oh-so-appropriate name for hosting football. Because in 1979 the Cosmos were a New York football team, famous for signing legendary players such as Pelé and Franz Beckenbauer. However, on the streets of Cosmos 79, where sheep still graze untethered by day, there are few who know of this historic fact.

La Paz Fútbol Club's motto is *Plus Altus*, "The Highest", and few grounds anywhere in the world are higher than the Los Andes stadium. From the stands, a stunning landscape greets the eye: the Cordillera Real, a mountain range with peaks stacked up one behind the other, and an average altitude of 6,000 metres. The home fans turn every match into a spectacle, and yet other teams remain reluctant to play so far away. Cosmos 79 is a half-hour microbus ride from La Ceja, which marks the border between El Alto and La Paz. The front line. The place where all roads leave and all roads lead.

Some have labelled El Alto "the non-city", due to it being some-what invisible, because it has no skyscrapers, no honey-coated streets with hundreds of neon signs, no other points of reference typical of modern-day towns. Because it's grey and dusty. Because it's over-run with roving traders and stray dogs. Yet it is, in fact, the most representative city in the country: peopled with folk from every corner, especially the countryside. And Cosmos 79 is inevitably a perfect microcosm.

You get to the neighbourhood through a street overrun with wood sellers. There are tyre-repair shops, avenues that seem as if they'll never end. There are painted warnings of what will happen to thieves: "Suspicious cars will be burnt," reads one of them. Hanging from several lamp posts are faceless rag dolls that likewise act as a warning to pickpockets. And one wrong turn in this desert of asphalt and brick can easily lead you astray, have you going round and round in circles for hours. Real Mamoré, the first professional team to play an away fixture in Los Andes, got lost on the way and kick-off had to be delayed.

"But that's no excuse for other teams not to come," laments Francisco Quispe, president of the Cosmos 79 Central Council of Residents' Associations. "If they're as good as they say they are, what are they scared of? The altitude? The artificial turf? It's really just because they're rubbish. The thing is, we haven't had proper football here since 1994."

Frenchman Albert Camus, a goalkeeper and wizard of the ball before becoming an essayist, novelist and tubercular, said: "For me, patriotism means the national football team." And in Bolivia, that patriotism has been left stuck in 1994.

The 1994 national team, the most acclaimed in Bolivian history, the only time Bolivia has ever qualified for the World Cup. As a team, they are so emblematic of the country that some members of the squad recently called for a lifelong annuity for services rendered. As though they'd risked their lives in some far-flung trench on the battlefield.

"If they want war, they'll get war," says Roberto Aguilar, manager of the El Alto Federation of Residents' Associations (Fejuve), seated on a wooden bench.

Fejuve's home is a pale building with chipped walls, a place constantly swallowing up and spitting out people. It's a thermometer that takes the temperature of *alteño* society. The headquarters of an organisation that, following a military massacre in 2003, forced President Gonzalo Sánchez de Lozada into exile.

At seventeen, the age when Messi began to triumph for Barcelona, Roberto Aguilar tells me he'd given up on the idea of becoming a footballer. The Spanish club paid for Messi's hormone treatment, costing the equivalent of US$900 a month. In Roberto's home, they couldn't afford boots or a regulation ball. And now Roberto's too old to play – he's around fifty – but not too old to enjoy football.

"My teammates and I are pretty much past it," he sighs, "but other *alteños* will play at the Los Andes stadium before long, the ones that do have a future." Then, sensing he's getting strange looks, he exclaims: "You play where you live, for Christ's sake!"

And his voice echoes down the corridor.

Football, I start to think, is also a question of democracy.

In 2007 Evo Morales caused an international stir by starting a crusade to prevent FIFA's Swiss president, Sepp Blatter, from banning stadiums over 2,500 metres. "If you can make love at altitude, then you can also play football," Evo reckoned, and to prove it, in a brush with madness, he organised a five-a-side match on the summit of Sajama, the country's roof at over 6,500 metres.

Cosmos 79's brush with madness came via a makeshift, last-minute kidnapping. A kidnapping in self-defence that the locals dreamt up from one minute to the next.

The last time I visited the Los Andes stadium, I was told nothing had been the same since they took top-flight football away, that the place felt odd. "The neighbourhood's got sadder" were the exact words. The light went out, like a candle that flickers and dies.

The picture that day told its own story: the streets practically empty, dust swirling in the wake of passing trucks, flashes of light reflecting off the rooftops. Down on the pitch a local junior league game, and barely any crowd.

Leaving the stands, I passed a middle-aged guy with a grizzly dry face and a woolly hat on his head, in neutral colours. He rode an old bicycle, a radio hanging from the rusty handlebars, swinging like a pendulum. The radio was tuned to commentary of the La Paz Fútbol Club game taking place at another stadium. Or to put it another way: the man was listening to a game they wouldn't let him watch at his own ground.

PABLO

5

Pablo Corso is thirty-three years old and lives in Buenos Aires, having spent his childhood and adolescence in Bariloche, Patagonia. He is a Communications graduate, a journalist and an Independiente fan. His *crónicas* and articles have been published in *Rolling Stone*, *Newsweek*, *Russia Beyond the Headlines*, *Brando* and *Caras & Caretas*. He worked as an editor on the daily newspaper *Crítica de la Argentina* and the magazine *El Guardián*. His Twitter account is @pablo_corso.

'The Team That's Always Robbed' ('*Este equipo siempre pierde por afano*') was first published in *El Guardián* in February 2011.

THE TEAM THAT'S ALWAYS ROBBED

Pablo Corso

Translated by Jonathan Blitzer

Outside the Campana prison walls all is calm and quiet, tidy; security is relaxed. The atmosphere and tension thicken with each closing padlock. At the end of a long, wide tunnel is a fully appointed garden, a school, a kitchen, grass pitches for bowls, football and rugby. Standing before the last set of bars, prison officer Daniel Martínez says that for the time being the inmates have a sense of purpose; the problems come when they're released. "If society doesn't help, this will always be the case." We're on our way to head coach Edgardo Sanabria's office. It's match day for the Pioneros, the first prison team to play in the AFA (Argentine Football Association) league.

Dark-haired and swarthy, Franco Zalazar acknowledges that the Pioneros have found it tough going so far: opposition players are more experienced, match-sharp, and in better physical shape. The twenty-nine-year-old holding midfielder will seek parole in ten months' time; he hopes to go and work in Atucha, where he has family. Hugo Hildenbrandt – a left-back with dye-streaked blond hair – says the team is always revved-up and spirited in training, but in the games they never quite feel at home. Daniel Mansilla has spent the last four years in jail. He wants to live with his three kids again and make up for the mistakes that brought him here: "Leaving lock-up for a while lets you forget about everything. In the games, we just want to devour the opposition." Eating is also on Luis Benítez's mind.

"What's changed since you started playing for the team?"

"Now I get to eat every day."

In the past, Benítez, who's spent three of his twenty-four years inside, had to make do with the classic mess-hall dish of *huesos recalentados*. These days he partakes of an improved diet of carbohydrates, fruit and vegetables.

The Pioneros evolved out of prison-yard kickabouts. "We'd seen the best guys play and we called them over to tell them they were going to form a team with the guards," says Miguel González, deputy director of security, former Pioneros head coach and current assistant coach. After several local friendlies – Caruso Lombardi, one of the best-known managers in the country, even brought a team along – an idea cropped up: why not enter a team in the Campana League? The Pioneros went on to win that league, earning themselves the right to compete in Zone 70 of the Argentine C League, the lowest rung of the official AFA championship. The C League is comprised of 319 teams from the country's interior, and offers three direct promotion places into the Argentine B League and three play-off berths.

After obtaining legal authorisation to field each player, Miguel had to do some financial juggling to keep the newfangled Club Deportivo Pioneros alive. The Campana town hall promised a subsidy of 1,500 pesos, not enough to cover a full season given the cost of every game: 1,800 pesos on referee fees, 800 to the AFA, 300 to the league, 600 to the regional security detail Coprosede ("they wanted nothing to do with us at first") and 1,200 to rent the Villa Dálmine pitch, where the Pioneros play their home games. The only sources of revenue are ticket and food sales.

The first game of the season, away to Everton in La Plata on January 23, was a complicated affair. Two police vehicles escorted the team bus to the ground. The players had to pass through a police cordon to enter the pitch, "and the police dogs came barrelling after them, they've a real nose for convicts," says Miguel. "Those hounds'll kill for coke," someone else says later. "Seriously, though, they will." Asides like this are repeated throughout the day. The deployment of 100 policemen was such an elaborate and protracted operation that the team ended up being fifteen minutes late for kick-off. The visit culminated in a 7-1 thrashing. A week later, at home to San Carlos de Capitán Sarmiento, the Pioneros lost 4-2. Their third game was perhaps the most devastating: an 8-1 loss to UTA of Luján.

The Pioneros train under the direction of coaches Marcos Colazo and Edgardo Sanabria. From Tuesday to Saturday, they have a general exercise period from 9:30 to 12:00 and football practice from 16:00 to 19:00. The squad is made up of twenty-three prisoners, with convictions for robbery, theft, kidnapping and extortion to their names (further details of their crimes can't be disclosed for legal reasons), five prison officers, a former inmate (goalkeeper Nazareno Garay) and a former prison guard. They range in age from nineteen to thirty-two. In Ezequiel Calegari's telling, at first there were a number of scuffles and disagreements between inmates and guards. They gradually came to an understanding: they were on the same side; they'd need to be. Calegari plays right-back and is in charge of the medium-security sector of the prison. Today he has a *mate* tea in hand and wears sandals, a laxity in appearance that suggests he won't be seeing action this afternoon.

The last door opens and the final padlock is fixed shut. We enter pavilion C2, a cement patio with a ribbed ceiling; clothes dry in sunlight that flits through the side beams; a refrigerator holds Tupperware filled with food. Seven cells border the patio, each one six feet by six feet and designed to house two inmates. The prisoners sleep two or three to a cell, on battered mattresses in precarious bunk beds (the top bunk has to be scaled from the floor – there is no ladder). There are television sets showing *Fútbol para Todos* and magazine cut-outs of silicon bombshells. Some cells have the privilege of cable television and Playboy TV. "If one of the boys gets too horny, we give him a good hiding," the inmates say.

Like all the cells, the one Ariel Aguilar (twenty-two years old, robbery conviction) calls home has a sheet-metal door with a bolt lock and a sliver of an opening in its centre. The cell has two broken fans and a shelf containing a bottle of shampoo, a gift from his family. Ariel seems affable and tries to smile through the rictus of depression. He has two months left of a four-year sentence. "We're all just kids who've suffered," he says, "but once you've been capped by the Pioneros, you have to stop feeling sorry for yourself." An inopportune look or a misplaced trainer can arouse the jealousy of the other inmates, those who don't get to play football, who eat badly and are treated worse.

In the centre of the pavilion, the Pioneros play hands of *truco* in groups of six. In a pre-match ritual card games alternate with confab. His shirt off, a constellation of tattoos visible on his chest and back, Alberto Kicherer pauses from the game to explain that he won't be playing for the Pioneros today, following a misunderstanding with the coach. In the last game Kicherer kicked out at someone, got a yellow card ("the ref gave them everything, so I gave them a bit back") and was immediately substituted. An argument ensued. Alberto regrets it now. "These kids are my friends. Football teaches you to have respect, to be smart, to show restraint." Lunch arrives: oven-cooked meat, some of it boiled, some breaded and fried. The food is served without any fuss. Fruit juice is passed around in big plastic jugs. It's a nice moment.

Mario "Manteca" Cortez, the Pioneros number 10, tells of a typical day in prison. He gets up at eight to have *mate* with his cellblock companions, then goes off to cook lunch for the bosses in the staff canteen. He used to work in the family paint shop, he says, keen to show he didn't always steal. He played in youth leagues in San Telmo and was on the verge of turning professional when he landed in jail. He can't play for the Pioneros because he's already registered for a team in Dolores, where he was previously imprisoned. He'll be the water boy this afternoon, but he still dreams of playing professionally when he gets out. Cristian Carrasco is less concerned with football and prison life than he is with making sure his photograph finds its way to "my future wife". Although they've only spoken on the telephone a few times, he's already keen to add her to his visitor list.

Coach Marcos Colazo stands to one side of the pavilion, though it's as if he isn't there: he has the panoptic gaze of all good prison guards. He's in charge of the Penitentiary Fire Prevention Unit, "because we get a lot of fires in here, you know?" After winning the league at Banfield de San Pedro, he set himself a new challenge. "We work on the humanitarian element more than anything else. There are guys in here who haven't been out on the street in seven years. Our opponents always expect to get the crap kicked out of them, that they'll be spat at and things like that, but they're always surprised; they end up saying these kids are all right." To be sure, he would also like to see some improvement on the pitch: "They lack a sense of direction. They're used to ranging around, getting dirty and having fun. The aim is to get them to feel comfortable, to play with freedom."

By two o'clock in the afternoon the Pioneros are getting restless. They want to be outside. The door opens and they assemble in lines. Beyond the last set of bars, the lights of the cameras from the programme *América* await them. In walks the beat reporter, Alfred, acting chummy. "Where's Pamela David? Bring her back!" is the beseeching refrain. Rifle-toting officials line the hundred-yard path to the hire bus. "Prisoner 15, Block 21! Prisoner 6, Block 41!"

shouts Miguel, calling the roll to the officers at the exit. En route to the game the collective excitement subsides as the players contemplate the landscape outside the bus windows. They gaze sadly at a world that has driven them to the brink.

The team's arrival at Villa Dálmine triggers a commotion that lasts nearly fifteen minutes. Police dogs lick their lips. Policemen surround the players. There's an officer stationed at every corner flag, as well as behind both goals. In total, eighty policemen surround the pitch, officers from the Buenos Aires Penitentiary Service, the Campana Units, the Transfers Department and the Canine Division. Home and away fans have to share the same terrace. The empty stand opposite looks the most precarious, and therefore doubles up as the most tempting avenue of escape. The 1981 film *Escape to Victory* comes to mind, the story of a football match between a German team and a team of concentration camp prisoners, featuring the likes of Sylvester Stallone, Michael Caine, Bobby Moore, Pelé and Osvaldo Ardiles.

The stakes aren't quite so high here. Sidelined because of a groin strain, prison guard Fabián Gamboa says he joined the team two years ago, got himself fit and scored six goals in his first season. He's played in the C League before, for Puerto Nuevo, and though he's now aged forty-one, he remains a prolific goal-scorer: he netted sixteen in last season's promotion campaign. "We don't have special authority on the team just because we wear the stripes," says fellow guard José Montenegro, who worked at "unsticking locks" and is now involved in sports administration at the prison. "Today we're all in it together, playing together, trying to move forward together. In any event, the team has already proved a success."

The Pioneros changing room is your typical Argentine changing room: white tiles, a fan battling against the heat, a couple of water coolers, a portrait of Christ presiding over the scene. In jeans and shirtsleeves, Marcos rallies his players: "We're on our own now, guys. What's past is past. We've worked hard all week. Now let's do what we've got to do. Let's show some intensity out there. If we can do it in training, why not here? Let's make sure it's three points to the home side this time!"

The Pioneros roar "Come on!" and then head down the tunnel and out onto the field. In the team huddle, where professional players tend to promise the impossible, centre-back Alberto Ríos hazards: "They play for money, we play for something more: out there is freedom." More prosaically, the goalie, Nazareno Garay, enjoins: "Do we want to play football or do we want to stay locked up?" The Everton players come out and drums sound from the Rio Platense fans. Eleven middle-class young men against eleven thugs with hanging heads and slumping postures.

The game begins. In the first minute, the Everton number 10 flattens the Pioneros number 2, a big lad with a commanding voice. The Everton player awkwardly attempts an apology. The game is evenly balanced, but you can sense the home side's jitters. The Pioneros coach rattles off calming words from the sidelines: "Relax, relax, relax!" Everton clatter into the Pioneros number 10, Lucas González, a skinny kid who writhes around on the ground before trying to get to his feet. A police dog has started barking and won't stop. The Pioneros number 4, Cristian Carrasco, wellies the ball forward. The coach warns him as he fumes at the referee.

The first Everton goal comes twenty-two minutes in. "Never mind, come on, keep your heads up," the coach exhorts. The game is a battle of grit versus agility. But the prospect of getting back on level terms gradually slips away. There's a spate of Everton goals – on thirty minutes, thirty-one, thirty-three and thirty-six. The Everton players are quicker and they find space, get in behind the Pioneros defence and win the ball in the box all too easily. The dog goes quiet. "A terrible silence," Oscar Ahumada, the Argentine international, might say. The Pioneros cut into the lead with a goal from number 11, and that sparks a further flurry of goals, with Everton scoring two more before half-time. "This is a mugging," someone chuckles in the stands. A family member tells the Pioneros to step it up a bit. They're giving it their all, reply their teammates from the bench. The Pioneros go into half-time 7-1 down.

Inside the dressing room, Marco is a man aflame. "I've nothing left to say; I've nothing left to say," he cries, and he paces around like Carlos Bilardo against Brazil in the 1990 World Cup in Italy. He points to nicknames ("Piturro", "Tubi", "Rata") on a torn sheet of paper. One of the players fires back: "With all due respect, you're not helping us." The complaint is drowned out by the coach's shouting. "They score and we give up. We may as well not bother turning up next time."

On come numbers 14, 15 and 16, the last being Montenegro, a guard. He has a few personal trademarks: he's the only player among the twenty-two with his shirt tucked into his shorts; he looks like a kempt, first-world policeman. Franco, with his dream of working in Atucha, is among the players to make way. He tries to communicate with his family in the stands. They show him his niece, Nicolle, who wants to give him a gift, a little drawing, and to tell him that she loves him. He says he loves her too – and also that he'd kill for a cigarette. A packet flies over the fence towards him. Two policewomen and their dogs stand between Franco and his family.

Everton's eighth goal comes six minutes into the second half; their ninth, seven minutes later. By now, the Pioneros right-back is in goal, doing what he can, the goalkeeper having had to go off injured. Sixteen minutes in, number 10 for the Pioneros is shown a red card for what we'll call an overly forceful challenge. Sitting on top of a Jabulani ball, the coach is true to his word and says nothing. When Everton's number 15 tries to prevent a free kick from being taken quickly, the Pioneros number 8 shoves him out of the way. Thirty-two minutes in, the score is sealed at 10-1. The Pioneros may not have played great football, but they showed spirit. Alejandro Almandi, the number 11, ran his socks off and fought for every ball. Bathed in sweat, the players file into the dressing room. Cristian Carrasco sums it up: "We lost our nerve as soon as they scored; it's infuriating. But we did our best."

After leaving the changing room, the team has five minutes to spend with their families. Under the attentive watch of policemen, disappointment at losing the game mixes with appreciation for contact with the outside world, as well as for the stealthy food parcels and plans for romantic rendezvous. Without their Pioneros shirts on, they're just kids anxious for the chance to pick up their lives, prisoners desperate for a change of scenery. But now dusk descends and they have to head back down a path of loaded Ithaca rifles and impregnable locks. The prisoners will contemplate the landscape again on the return journey. They'll sleep stacked in bunk beds. They'll dream of Pamela David, and a future free of drubbings, with no goals scored against them.

Surya Lecona Moctezuma is a Mexican freelance journalist focused on human-rights issues and current affairs across Latin America. She loves non-fiction, *crónicas* and old typewriters. She has contributed to numerous publications, including *Replicante*, *Expansión*, *La Otra Orilla*, *El Financiero* and *De Largo Aliento*. She is part of the editorial board on the magazine *Spleen! Journal* and co-author of *Tú y yo coincidimos en la noche terrible*, a book focused on 127 journalists who have disappeared or been killed in Mexico.

'Costa Nica: The Central American Dream' (*'Costa Rica, Costa Nica, Costa Risueña'*) was first published in March 2013 in *Replicante*.

COSTA NICA: THE CENTRAL AMERICAN DREAM

Surya Lecona Moctezuma

Translated by Ruth Clarke

"Over here, bitch!"

I was taken aback the first time I heard it. We were on a bus and that was how the woman in front of me addressed her daughter. But having my Costa Rican friends call me "bitch" soon stopped sounding strange or offensive.

In deprived and marginalised areas you hear *güila* (bitch) used all the time to refer to girls, and *pendejo* (dick) attributed to anyone, male or female, who's a bit of a grouch, a crybaby or a wuss. Unlike back home in Mexico, neither *güila* nor *pendejo* is considered offensive.

All the same, women in Costa Rica suffer the effects of machismo just as keenly as women in Mexico. Heredia is a city in the Valle Central, the country's central area, and *Ticos* (Costa Ricans) hail Heredia's females as the nation's pride and joy, the prettiest in all the land, much like Mexicans champion women from Guadalajara. Similarly, when it comes to football, *Ticos* from Heredia are just as passionate as *chivas* from Guadalajara.

Outside Heredia's stadium a policeman gives me the following tip: "Buy your tickets from the sellers outside the ground, you'll see them everywhere. Don't bother with the ticket office." This is not a simple matter of the police cynically colluding to help touts double or triple their money, as is commonplace in Mexico. There's more to it than that. Heredia's players have gone several months without being paid; the extra money made from unauthorised ticket sales finds its way back to the players, to compensate for their missing wages.

"So, are Heredia at home on Sunday?"

"Well, only if they pay the electric," the chef at the Casa Azul bar tells me, despairingly.

The club is in crisis. According to *La Nación*, a local newspaper, on the day Heredia learnt they were officially the best club in Central America, according to rankings produced by the International Federation of Football History and Statistics, their Eladio Rosabal stadium was closed down because the club had failed to make its social security payments and was behind on its employment insurance premiums and contributions to the Heredia Public Services Company.

At a recent game against Saprisa, Heredia fans hurled insults at the team's owner, as well as at Saprisa's owner, Vergara. Vergara? Yes, the same Vergara who owns the Chivas! Up until a year ago, Jorge Carlos Vergara Madrigal owned both clubs. Rivalries being what they are, Mexican football is loathed and distrusted in equal measure by football fans in Costa Rica; "Costa Ridiculous", as local novelist Carlos Cortés would have it; "Costa Radiant", as Mexican journalist Pablo Pérez-Cano prefers.

The unrolled Costa Rican "R" is a trait so specific to a *Tico* from Valle Central that they consider it something to be proud of. Primary school teachers take the blame, for not teaching children tongue twisters like "round the rugged rock the ragged rascal ran", staples of early learning in Spain and Mexico. But the constant flow of migrants may also have played a role in softening the "R"s.

Costa Rica is a mixed-up place. It aspires to be European, but there's no escaping the influence of Latino immigrants, be it in the accents or in the Colombian shops displaying signs for "bum-lifting jeans in a wide range of styles and sizes".

Migration is a major issue – another parallel with Mexico. Costa Rica, at the heart of Central America, is "one of the most peaceful countries in the world", according to its inhabitants, and this is something they're very proud of. But *Nicas* (Nicaraguans) have long been making their way south, and they suffer discrimination and xenophobia throughout the country. The disdain with which *Nicas* are treated by *Ticos* is perhaps a consequence of the fact that, historically speaking, there has been minimal coexistence between ethnic groups in Costa Rica: the country's indigenous population is almost non-existent, registering a token one per cent of the population, the same as Chinese; three per cent of the population is black, with ninety-four per cent classed as white or mixed race.

The migration phenomenon can easily be seen on the streets of San José, with a multitude of nationalities sharing the same pavement. The destitute wander the city's arteries and the homeless lie motionless on the tarmac, huddled up in foetal positions with only cardboard and rags to protect them from the elements. All await the opportunity of a home, a job, a life.

There are many factors related to homelessness, not least the disparity between the minimum wage and high rental rates. The current average monthly salary for a domestic worker is the equivalent of US$250 while the cost of renting a room can be upwards of US$150, making for a severe lack of purchasing power.

"Save your prayers for Saint Peter and your begging for Granny to take you in – we don't want any more tramps here!" yells a police officer with a fascist glare, as he hammers his truncheon against the metal structure beneath which Virginia Araya and her son, Álvaro Fuentes, have been sleeping. They've come to the capital from

Alajuela, to visit a hospital that might be able to treat Virginia for a leg problem, phlebitis, which has confined her to a wheelchair at the age of sixty-five. Her hands shake and you can sense the anxiety in her cold skin and timid voice. She tries to explain that they're just trying to get some rest, but gets a blow to the head for her troubles. A security guard from the bank on the high street has already moved them on once tonight, rattling their cardboard shelter with his stick and forcing them to move their makeshift home further down the pavement.

Immigration is most evident in the shanty towns, known in Costa Rica as *precarios*. Carpio and León XIII lie on the San José outskirts, two *precarios* where, according to your average Costa Rican, not even the police, ambulance and fire services set foot. Ghettos of Chinese, Dominicans, Nicaraguans, Salvadorians and Colombians dominate. The majority of the inhabitants are second-generation immigrants, born in Costa Rica to incomer parents.

"León XIII is the worst *precario* in the country in terms of drug addiction, violence, illiteracy and delinquency," says Suyapa Cuadros, who runs a project in District 4 of León XIII's Tibas canton. The *Asociación de Cultura y Recreación de León XIII* offers workshops in football, rap and painting, among other things. At three in the afternoon, Sabana Park is full of children and young people. They come and go, changing shifts on the concrete terraces and the ragged pitch, worn thin by the neighbourhood's football and basketball players. A football match is under way between teams from León XIII and Carpio. Their bright new kits disguise their physical appearances, making their tattoos, piercings and gel-set Mohicans more presentable. The green Costa Rican field both frames and hides the troubles these young people face. The game ends and the players lie down on the grass sipping water. Before heading home, they search in vain for a mobile phone that went missing while they were playing.

Football is everywhere, a constant running through all communities. All the youngsters in León XIII are big football fans and most play *mejenga*, or street football, while others fashion home-made shotguns, known as *chizas*.

Giovanni is fifteen, though he'd pass for eighteen if it weren't for his acne. He comes across as mild-mannered and considerate. He's been smoking marijuana since the age of eleven and making guns since he was twelve. "You make *chizas* out of iron tubes and pellet guns; you put the tube on top and fit a sharp nail and spring coil, or part of an old bicycle, to fire it. It's enough to kill a person." Giovanni explains this to me calmly, and admits that before he'd turned twelve he'd held .32, .38 and 9 mm guns, and that he used to roam the streets of central San José with them, mugging people, holding up buses and stealing mobile phones. "But I was just a kid then, and kids make a lot of mistakes," he says. "Now I want to learn computing and get myself on *feisbuc*."

Alan (not his real name) is sixteen years old. He tells me he first fired a gun aged thirteen, in a revenge attack following the stabbing of a cousin. "I was a kid, I wanted to play the hero and so I bought a nine millimetre for sixty thousand colones [US$30], shot the guy and then sold the gun on again for eighty thousand colones," he tells me, all the while worrying that his identity will be revealed. He's smoked marijuana, crack and freebase. "I also injected heroin once," he says, before jerking away from the Dictaphone as gunfire suddenly rings out. "Don't worry, they know children play in the park so they don't come down here," he says to reassure me, albeit from behind the cement bench he had been sitting on. He laughs: "I'm only hiding down here just in case."

The sound of fourteen gunshots sends people running to the park's wire fence. Rumours start to fly, but the *mejenga* goes on. The players rotate constantly. Some are in great physical shape, others not so much. The older ones play dirty, lashing out and threatening their opponents. Oscar, one of the best players, is also one of the youngest; he's eleven years old, has already tried marijuana and seen the guns his brothers carry. "It's nothing to be scared of," Oscar shouts to those of us running away. "Gunshots are like fireworks round here."

I find out later that the gunfire we heard was "El Cuello" (The Neck), one of the most notorious armed robbers in León XIII, being "burnt". "Burnt" is another word you hear all the time: it means being shot in the foot.

Leonardo Haberkorn is a Uruguayan journalist and the Associated Press correspondent in Montevideo. He has worked for a range of media outlets in Uruguay and has had pieces published in several leading Latin American magazines, including *Gatopardo* (Colombia/Mexico) and *Etiqueta Negra* (Peru), and in the anthologies *Crónicas de otro planeta: las mejores historias de Gatopardo* (Mexico, 2009), *Para gritar, para cantar, para llorar* (Chile, 2010) and *Antología de crónica latinoamericana actual* (Spain, 2012). His books include *Milicos y tupas*, which won the Bartolomé Hidalgo and Libro de Oro prizes in 2011.

'Run, Ghiggia, Run' ('*Corre Ghiggia, corre!*') was first published in *Gatopardo* (No. 32, Colombian edition) in 2002.

RUN, GHIGGIA, RUN

Leonardo Haberkorn

Translated by Tim Girven

Alcides Edgardo Barreiro, Alcides Edgardo Bentancor, Alcides Edgardo Caraballo, Alcides Edgardo Chans, Alcides Edgardo Di Ciocco... the Uruguayan phone book is full of people called Alcides Edgardo, named in honour of World Cup winner Alcides Edgardo Ghiggia, whose exploits are familiar to all Uruguayans – and Brazilians.

Perhaps that's why the news hit so hard. "Ghiggia sells medals of his glorious sporting past", ran the headline in the daily *La República* on June 5. "Ghiggia," said the story, "was having to let go of mementos accumulated over the course of his glorious sporting past, putting his medals up for sale in order to resolve pressing financial problems..."

The most valuable medal was sold for the equivalent of US$1,600 and was bought by an individual employed by Tenfield, Paco Casal's sports-broadcasting business. Casal is a controversial figure: football magnate, agent to the vast majority of Uruguay's footballers and owner of the TV rights to all UFA (Uruguayan Football Association) activities. The $1,600 medal was the one Ghiggia won for his Brazilian exploits.

It all happened on July 16, 1950, the day Brazil played Uruguay in the World Cup final. The match was played before 200,000 people at the Maracanã stadium, which had been built especially for the occasion. The Brazilians were hosting the World Cup with the aim of becoming World Champions for the first time, and they were on the verge of achieving it.

The Brazilian team had won its two previous games by record margins: 6-1 against Spain and 7-1 against Sweden, apparent confirmation that the team was invincible. Uruguay, the other finalist, had narrowly overcome the Swedes 3-2 and only managed a 1-1 draw with Spain. Brazil's coronation as World Champions was a *fait accompli*, the game against Uruguay a mere formality.

But things didn't turn out the way everyone expected, and the main reason was Ghiggia.

The Brazilians didn't know him very well. They knew all about Obdulio Varela, the veteran Uruguayan captain, whose mettle was legendary. But Ghiggia was young and new to the national side, having only broken into Peñarol's first team the year before. When he arrived in Brazil for the World Cup, he was still wet behind the ears in international terms. But he'd scored in Uruguay's first game, and then in the second, and again in the third. Even today, he appears in FIFA's statistics as one of only two players to score in every game and reach the World Cup final.

The fourth game he scored in was the final.

Las Piedras is twenty-five miles from Montevideo. It's a small town surrounded by farmland and vineyards, populated by white- and blue-collar workers who get up early and go to work in the capital. A modest town for modest people. Ghiggia has lived there for some three or four years, since leaving Montevideo.

Everyone knows him. They say that to find him you've to ask for him at the last stall in the market, beside the railway line.

Las Piedras' market is a refuge of the unemployed. Some erect their little stalls to try and earn a living selling bric-a-brac. Others go there to spend what few pesos they have.

Two whole blocks sell the cheapest of products: clothing "Made in China", shoes with fake brands, suspicious-looking whiskies from Brazil, contraband soft drinks. The last stall, which sells cheap baby clothes, is run by a young woman. She's the old champ's wife.

Ghiggia was Uruguay's right-winger. In the dressing room, before the game, the manager instructed Ghiggia's teammates to feed him the ball as often as possible, via long balls over the top, for his pace was the team's trump card. "They discussed team tactics and agreed on a game plan whereby play would focus on the right. He [Ghiggia] was at his physical prime, he had excellent technique, and it was clear to all that he feared neither man nor beast," relates Franklin Morales in his book *Maracanã: The Labyrinths of Character*, the most comprehensive study of the events of that day. The first half ended 0-0, but Brazil scored a minute after the restart. Everyone expected another Brazil goal to follow, and another and another and another, but then Ghiggia came to life.

In the sixty-fifth minute, Obdulio passed him the ball. The winger left his marker, Bigode, for dead, and headed for goal. As he burst into the Brazilian penalty area, he put in a precise cross for Alberto Schiaffino to get on the end of and level the score.

If the game finished all square, Brazil would be crowned champions. But thirteen minutes later, Ghiggia escaped with the ball once again and embarked on an electrifying run that lasted barely six seconds but which – more than half a century later – is still known to football fans everywhere.

Since then, every July 16, Uruguayan radio stations broadcast the commentary of that decisive attack, perhaps the most mythical in the history of the World Cup:

"Tejera defends. It comes back to Danilo. Danilo loses out to Julio Pérez, who immediately plays a pass over to Míguez. Míguez returns it to Pérez, who battles with Jair, still inside the Uruguayan half. He gives it to Ghiggia. Ghiggia plays it back to Julio Pérez who hits it long down the right channel. Run, Ghiggia! Run, Ghiggia! He bears down on the Brazilian goal, and shoots! Goal! Goal for Uruguay! Ghiggia! A second goal for Uruguay. Uruguay are winning two-one..."

The revelation that Ghiggia had auctioned his Maracanã medal unleashed a storm in Montevideo.

El País, the most influential and highest-circulation newspaper in Uruguay, wrote two editorials on the subject in as many days. It said news of the auction "shook every Uruguayan to the core" and called upon everyone to contribute in order to resolve "the difficult economic situation Ghiggia was experiencing". Not everyone agreed and the controversy grew. In the weekly *Búsqueda* a reader wrote in to say Ghiggia didn't deserve such help: "Selling off his medal is an insult: it's a question of ethics; some things just aren't for sale!" Despite all this, the press managed the story with a degree of restraint. In contrast to what would have happened in neighbouring Argentina, none of the media delved into the nature of Ghiggia's economic woes or looked into what had motivated this desperate act, nor did they publish details of his private life, of which the public knew little. Instead, most papers directed their inky ire against the state, at the country as a whole for failing to provide for its great champion.

"The people and the country never gave him the material support he ought to have received for being a true legend," wrote one businessman, who announced that he was disposed to buy the medal in order to return it to Ghiggia.

In fact, such was the demand for better official support for Ghiggia that the vice-minister for Education and Culture was obliged to appear on television and detail all the benefits the country had given the 1950 World Cup winners.

In the meantime, the story had become international news. That same June 5, the *Folha de São Paulo* reported news of the auction on its website, while the *Corriere della Sera*'s June 9 edition carried the following headline: "Ghiggia living in poverty, forced to sell everything just to survive."

"With none of his countrymen prepared to help him out, he's been forced to 'pawn his glory' just to put food on the table. When did solidarity die?" wrote the Italian journalist.

Ghiggia was once well-to-do. Born to a middle-class family in 1926, during Uruguay's golden age, he wanted for nothing in childhood.

He played basketball in his teens, but later turned to football, and by the age of twenty-one he'd signed for Peñarol, which, alongside Nacional, is one of the giants of Uruguayan football. He won the league in his first full season in yellow and black, and his exceptional ability and speed soon saw him break into the national team. Following the Maracanã triumph, he won the league with Peñarol again in 1951, by which time he was earning a pretty good wage. "At Peñarol I earned eight hundred pesos a month. And that was good money: look, me and another lad used to go out drinking with ten pesos and we were like kings. I think the peso was on a par with the dollar back then," Ghiggia related in one of the few interviews he's given in Uruguay in recent years.

In 1953 he left Peñarol to play for Roma in Italy. Very few South American players were contracted to European teams at the time, but after his performance at the Maracanã, Ghiggia had become a figure of world standing.

His signing marks a before-and-after in the history of the Italian club. On Roma's official club webpage, journalist Franco Dominici tells of Ghiggia's arrival in Italy. A telegram confirmed the transfer from Peñarol just as Roma's president, Renato Sacerdoti, was addressing a gathering of fans. When he was handed the telegram, he broke off the discussion and called for silence. When everyone had fallen quiet, he made the following solemn announcement: "A few hours ago, we finalised the signing of a famous world champion: Alcides Ghiggia!" The assembly erupted in thunderous applause.

On July 13, 1953, scores of Roma supporters waited to greet Ghiggia at the airport. Expectations were so high that the following day, 55,000 *tifosi* turned out to see him make his debut in a friendly against the English side Charlton Athletic. Ghiggia still hadn't signed a contract, but he couldn't resist playing.

He remained in Italy for nine years: eight seasons with Roma (with whom he won the Inter-Cities Fairs Cup) and one for Milan (with whom he won the Italian league). Given the quality of his performances, and taking advantage of his Italian ancestry, he was called up to play for the Italian national team. Economically he was better-off in Italy than he ever was at Peñarol. "I earned more in Italy," he related in the same interview. "I made twelve million lire in two years. I don't know how much that is, but I know it agreed with me."

"The most incredible thing about the man is that, given all that he earned in life, he had nowhere to live!" says his wife, as she leads the way to the house they share.

They were married two years ago and have lived together for six. She's now thirty years old, while Ghiggia, although he appears much younger, has already celebrated his seventy-fifth birthday. They met each other at a driving school in Las Piedras, where, until relatively recently, the hero of the Maracanã gave driving lessons.

Ask Ghiggia how a man of his age can win over a thirty-year-old woman, and he just smiles. Inside their small rented home, five young women – film students – surround Ghiggia and explain that they want to make a film about his life. The athlete gives his consent.

The furniture is cheap, but everything is clean and tidy. There's a telephone and a fridge, and a stereo that's too big for the place.

But there are no family photos on the mantelpiece, no pictures of Ghiggia's two sons or his four grandchildren. Instead, there is a gigantic portrait of the man himself, from the time when he was world champion, and a dozen little plaques and trophies that all feature the same two words: Ghiggia and Maracanã.

Ghiggia doesn't wear Italian fashion labels like the Uruguayan footballers of today, though he's not badly dressed. His clothes are not expensive, but they're new, they're clean and ironed, and the colours work well together.

Physically, Ghiggia keeps himself in impeccable physical shape. He says he goes out for a jog on the quiet streets of Las Piedras every afternoon, and until not long ago he still played five-a-side. And he dyes his hair so that it looks as black as it did in the days when he played for Roma. "Life was very good back then. Rome is a beautiful city, I liked it a lot, the old part as well as the new part, which I saw grow. But it was also a time of living life in public, of very little intimacy or privacy, of being constantly hassled by the paparazzi, you know? They were always around, they followed you day and night – especially at night, obviously. You'd go out at midnight and there'd be a whole troop of paparazzi following along behind. And life was full of temptations; it was a mad, mad time – madness!"

This was how Ghiggia summed up his near decade in Italy in a booklet biography published by *El País*, to mark the fiftieth anniversary of the Maracanã triumph. Ghiggia recounts in the book that when he lived in Rome he had three Alfa Romeos: first a Superleggera coupé, then a convertible, and finally a Giulietta. That he used to go and watch the boxing. That he saw Cassius Clay crowned Olympic champion in the Palacio de los Deportes. That he often went to Cinecittà. That he knew Anna Magnani, Gina Lollobrigida...

Ghiggia doesn't like to speak about any of this very much. If asked about life in Rome, he gives brief answers and changes the subject. Franco Dominici is rather more effusive in his account of the club's history. "Ghiggia played well, he shone, people liked him, but he never quite managed to have a decisive impact. He had the natural majesty of a World Cup winner; he fell crazily in love with Rome and thought he could conquer the city with his dribbling; he lived days of plenty – long afternoons, distant horizons, endless places to discover.

"He liked being the centre of attention.

"He opened a bar in Via del Tritone, off Piazza Barberini; he made a series of ill-judged investments [...] He left Roma after eight seasons, 201 games and ten goals – very few, in truth. So did Ghiggia disappoint? Absolutely not: he wasn't an out-and-out striker, everyone knew that, and in Rome he proved himself an inspired creator. But there were difficult moments, above all due to a troubled family life, and considerable complications related to his business activities. In summary, Ghiggia was not very astute at managing his own affairs, nor did he choose his advisers, friends and partners wisely. In Rome he was much loved, he became very popular, but not very rich. On the contrary."

Ghiggia returned to Uruguay in 1963. All the other Maracanã victors had retired by then, all except him. His exceptional physical condition and technical ability allowed him to go on playing into his forties. Franklin Morales declares Ghiggia the most physically gifted player he ever saw. "He had really long legs and a small upper body, like an acrobat's, and he was almost impossible to knock over – he never went to ground. His stride was huge and he ran like a greyhound. He also had unfailing courage. The more he got kicked, the better he got. There was never another forward like him."

Ghiggia played in the Uruguayan first division – for the clubs Danubio and Sud América – until late 1968. He retired seven days shy of his forty-second birthday.

Upon leaving football, Ghiggia had two houses: one in El Pinar – a spa town – and the other in Montevideo, but not enough money not to have to work. The glory days were over.

As the vice-minister of Education and Culture explained, when told Ghiggia had auctioned his medal, the state had given Ghiggia the same support it gave his teammates: he was given a public sector job, in Ghiggia's case in a municipal casino, where he worked until 1990, when he retired. The state also granted him what's known in Uruguay as a "discretionary pension": a form of monthly subsidy awarded by parliament to citizens of particular merit. These days, between this special allowance and his pension, Ghiggia receives some 1,500 pesos a month, which – even taking recent devaluations into account – is the equivalent of US$535, considerably more than what most Uruguayans earn.

Ghiggia has never lacked these two incomes and yet he's still had to sell his possessions. First the house in El Pinar. Then the house in Montevideo. Then the medal from the Maracanã.

"The man is a disaster with money," says his wife. She explains that she now insists he administer his affairs better. "With the money he was paid for the book [the equivalent of US$6,000], I made him buy a car, otherwise the money would have just vanished..."

Cars and women: two passions that have always been with him. "I've always loved cars," he says in his biography. And those who've known him say Ghiggia has always had a weakness for women too.

He bought his first car as a Peñarol player, a Ford Perfect, which he later changed for a Ford B8, and then for a Pontiac, the car he owned when he met his first wife, on the seafront promenade in Montevideo.

He married her in 1952 and they went to Italy together. A journalist from the daily *Il Mattino* recalled the strong impression his beautiful wife made when descending from the aeroplane ("his astonishing creole spouse").

Then came the Alfa Romeo period, and with it a number of difficulties.

Ghiggia was accused of seducing an underage girl in one of the cars and, although he was acquitted, had to defend himself in the Italian courts. Ghiggia has said that it was all just a clumsy attempt to extort money from him.

Upon returning to Montevideo he divorced. His two children – who did not remain in Italy, as many Uruguayans believe – were born of this first, failed matrimony. But they prefer not to talk about their father. His daughter, Lilián, the owner of a beauty salon, emphatically refused the offer of an interview. She said that neither she nor her brother Arcadio, nor even their mother, ever spoke to the press, and that they never would; with that, very annoyed, she hung up.

Ghiggia married again and was widowed in 1992. Then in 1996, at the driving school, he began to give classes to a young woman. The pair say they liked each other right away and decided to live together. Later they married. And she advised him to buy another car – second-hand, of course.

In the last few minutes of the 1950 World Cup final, before a silenced Maracanã that sensed tragedy, Ghiggia tormented the Brazilians.

"Bauer passes it back to Juvenal. The ball goes out to Ghiggia! He receives it on the right wing. He moves forward slowly, walking – he's in no hurry. He's slowing the game right down. Here comes Bigode. Ghiggia dances with the ball. To the left, to the right. The ball remains glued to the Uruguayan forward's foot. He sidesteps Bigode and passes to Julio Pérez, who gives it back to Ghiggia..."

Morales recounts in his book that the exasperated Uruguayan manager had to beg Ghiggia to stop attacking and help his teammates defend.

"The crazy fool wants a third," the coach reputedly said.

At the final whistle, Obdulio sought Ghiggia out and raised him to his shoulders. The journalist Antonio Pippo, author of a biography of the Uruguayan captain, recounts that, though Obdulio was notoriously a man of few words, he twice told him that:

"If it wasn't for Ghiggia, we'd have never won that game."

Schiaffino too, perhaps the most refined player of that World Cup-winning side, said much the same thing in an interview with the daily *El Observador*. "What was the difference between you and the Brazilians?"

"Ghiggia. He played brilliantly. He imposed himself on the game – he was outstanding!... He destroyed anyone who tried to mark him... He may be small, but he's tough, and oh, how he ran..."

Without doubt, the Brazilians have been quicker to recognise Ghiggia's worth than have the Uruguayans, who tend to put the 1950 win down as a triumph of "Uruguayan guts" rather than a victory of great football (and so, for us, it remains).

The Brazilians, on the other hand, despite their pain, have shown a better understanding of what really happened that day.

Ghiggia recounts that the last time he visited Brazil, in 2001, his passport was checked by a young lady who was about twenty-five years old. When she saw his name, she went quiet for ten long seconds. Then she asked:

"Sir, are you *the* Ghiggia?"

"Yes."

"From the 1950 final?"

"It was a long time ago..."

"Yes, but we still feel the pain in our hearts."

Today, Brazil are the World Cup holders. Five-time champions. Ghiggia's wife takes the film students off to visit the places where they'll shoot their film. Ghiggia sits down in an armchair and warns me that he charges for interviews.

"I rarely give interviews to Uruguayan journalists because they won't pay. They say they don't have the money, but foreigners always cough up. They've come from Argentina, from Brazil, from Peru, from North America, and I always make them pay."

It's true. A few years ago, a foreign film-maker came to film him as part of a documentary on the greatest footballers of all time, and paid him US$6,000. I explain to Ghiggia that although I'm Uruguayan, the article I'm writing is for a prestigious Colombian magazine and that it's a good opportunity for me. Ghiggia agrees to speak for free this time:

"I don't want you to lose out on an opportunity to publish an article abroad. But let it be known that Ghiggia always gets paid."

"Do you have money problems?"

"No, I'm not complaining. I get my pension from the casino and a gratuity the government awarded us. Given the state the country's in right now, you can't ask for more than that."

"Do you feel Uruguayans no longer value what you and your teammates achieved?"

"Uruguay has forgotten the Maracanã, it only remembers every July 16. But it doesn't bother me. I know what I did and didn't do. I did my patriotic duty."

Ghiggia laughs. He explains that he was born before his time, that if he'd played in Italy today he'd have been a millionaire. But he says it doesn't bother him, that he doesn't miss the fame or the fortune, and that he just wants to live a quiet life with his family. What does bother him is that people are always delving into his private life. That they say he's impoverished. That they write that he owned a bar in Italy. That they report that he sold off his Maracanã World Cup winner's medal. "It's not true. The journalist who wrote that didn't come here and see me, did he?

If he'd have paid me a visit, I'd have shown him I still have the medal right here."

(The truth of the matter is that the medal was sold, but also that Ghiggia still has it. "It's a sad story, very sensitive, something we'd prefer not to speak about," said a functionary at Gomensoro, the auctioneering firm that handled the sale. But he does confirm two things: that the auction took place, and that the person who bought the medal gave it back to Ghiggia. He's the Maracanã champion, after all.)

Ghiggia prefers talking about football, about his career, about the famous Peñarol team of 1949, about the goal he scored in the 1950 World Cup final, about how he barely celebrated in the Maracanã because he went straight to the showers, unaware of what a momentous thing he'd achieved, about how he adapted to European football...

"I played until I was forty-two... And they say I lived a wicked life! How can anyone play until that age living a wicked life!"

"But is it true he liked women a lot?"

"Who doesn't like women a lot? I wasn't a womaniser, but I was young, I dressed well..."

The aspiring young film-makers have returned. Ghiggia receives them with a smile and a joke. He says the journalist has just paid him a thousand dollars and that now it's their turn. The interview comes to an end. Ghiggia accompanies me to the door and down the path. For my last question, I ask him why he didn't attend the funeral of Julio Pérez, another of the 1950 World Cup winners, who'd died a few days previously.

"I went to the wake, but I don't like burials," he says. We don't know it then, but by the end of the week, Eusebio Tejera, another of the "Lions of the Maracanã", will also be gone.

As we say our goodbyes, a neighbourhood girl passes by and Ghiggia shares a joke with her. Then he turns and goes back to the house. He has to climb a few steps to get to the front door. He does so with great agility, practically running up them, as if to show he's still the unstoppable winger.

He goes inside, into the little living room bearing the huge portrait of himself as champion of the world.

Clara Becker is from Rio de Janeiro. She is a Botafogo fan and a reporter for the magazine *Veja Brasília*. She worked for *piauí* magazine from 2009 to 2013.

'Congressman Romário: Big Fish in the Aquarium' ('*Peixe no aquário*') was first published in *piauí* in January 2012.

CONGRESSMAN ROMÁRIO: BIG FISH IN THE AQUARIUM

Clara Becker

Translated by Robin Patterson

It's ten o'clock on a November morning and, with twenty-four federal congressmen and one senator on board, the bus sets out from the Holiday Inn in Porto Alegre in the direction of Canoas, on the outskirts of the city. First, however, the bus has to double back and pick up one more legislator at the airport. Congressman Romário de Souza Faria couldn't come down the night before because he was at a birthday party for his fourth child, Rafinha. The boy's mother, from whom Romário is separated, insisted he turn up, even though the actual birthday isn't until February.

Romário greets his colleagues glumly and quickly sits down on his own at the back of the bus. He pulls the curtain closed and puts on dark glasses, completely absorbed in his mobile phone. He only takes his eyes off it when the group starts making fun of Francisco Escórcio, a federal congressman from Maranhão, better known as Chiquinho, who's standing up at the front near the driver, making some sort of speech. Someone shouts out: "Francisco, tell me something, that suit you're wearing – did you get it off the *Professor Raimundo* comedy show?" Everyone creases up laughing, including

Chiquinho. Romário smiles for the first time, stands up and leads the chant: "Oids, oids, oids, Chiquinho haemorrhoids."

"Behave yourself!" retorts Chiquinho. "You've only just turned up and right away you want a window seat? The rest of us have already done half a day's work." The bus ride is turning into a school outing. Congressman Renan Filho pulls a pink football boot out of his bag. It looks like a giant-sized Barbie accessory, and someone calls him a poof. "Jean Wyllys gave it to me," he replies. "Bolsonaro thinks it looks gay."

A long-time ally of José Sarney, the former president and now leader of the Senate, Chiquinho was previously a senator and special adviser to Renan Calheiros, but was sacked on suspicion of spying on the opposition. He recently discovered that congressmen were arranging kickabouts on Tuesday afternoons, straight after the session in the Chamber, and immediately sensed their popular appeal. "I realised there was political gain to be had from big names like Romário, Popó and Tiririca," he said.

He was right – the Solidarity Games he set up are a huge success. Matches pitching federal and state legislators against each other are held all over Brazil and the money they raise is donated to charity. With no end of congressmen trying to get the team to visit their own electoral fiefdoms, there are already more than twenty requests for matches. "We'll have to draw fixtures out of a hat," says Chiquinho, who is already planning an international career for the team. This time round, the congressmen are playing in Canoas and São Leopoldo, down in the state of Rio Grande do Sul. Their host, Marco Maia, the Speaker of the Chamber (the lower house in the federal legislature), plays the first ten minutes of each game. Despite the threats ("If you don't pass the ball to the speaker, he'll take you off the committee! You've got to pass to the speaker!"), Maia is off form. He feigns an injury and leaves the pitch without managing a goal.

The presence of Romário, ex-boxer Acelino "Popó" Freitas and former footballers Deley and Danrlei ensures there'll be spectators. Their next match, as guests of Edison Lobão, the Minister of Mines and Energy, will be in Imperatriz, up in the far-northern state of Maranhão, in two weeks' time. The minister gets to present the trophy to the winners.

Romário plays in the Solidarity Games only on condition that the profits are given to charities that help people with disabilities, one of the main causes he champions in Congress. As he's the star attraction, nobody objects. "I went into politics with three clear aims: supporting people with disabilities, fighting drugs and controlling spending on the 2014 World Cup," he explains. "Nothing's going to distract me from that."

The bus makes two stops in Canoas before the game. The congressmen visit the local branches of the Association of Parents and Friends of Exceptional People and the Pestalozzi Institute. "See how Romário has already gone all dewy-eyed? He always gets emotional," observes Sérgio Petecão, one of the senators from Acre. A member of the Chamber before moving to the upper house, he's the only senator in the team. At over six feet tall, he makes a useful central defender.

"We come here to cleanse our souls and forget about all the problems back home," confesses Congressman Protógenes Queiroz, holding a child on his lap. Protógenes is a district superintendent "on leave" from the Federal Police following a criminal conviction, while on the pitch he's a winger, known for addressing the ball as "Your Excellency". The role of team policeman now goes to Popó, Romário's strike partner, who "never passes when he gets the ball". Protógenes pushes his way through a crowd of people so that the child he's carrying, who has walking difficulties, can have his photo taken with his idol, Romário.

"You, the mothers, need to put pressure on the politicians," explains Romário to the dozens of women standing around him. He calls Marco Maio over: "And just to prove this trip isn't a waste of time, all the congressmen here are promising to set aside for these organisations some of the money saved from the budget amendments, isn't that right?" Marco Maia nods, smiling wanly.

"I see myself as a voice on the inside, representing parents with kids like mine. I know what they need," says Romário. Soon after the birth of his youngest daughter (his sixth child, from four different women), a doctor took him aside and told him that the little girl had been born with some sort of syndrome, though they weren't yet sure which. Romário held back the tears, went into the room and said to his wife, Isabella Bittencourt: "God has given us a special baby."

When she learnt that the girl, Ivy, had Down's syndrome, Isabella was afraid her husband would leave her. "Unfortunately that sort of thing happens," she told me. To her surprise, having Ivy has made Romário more responsible, and the two of them are inseparable. He says he doesn't want to do anything that would disappoint her; he wants his daughter to be proud of her dad.

The pre-match lunch of steaks and beer goes some way to explaining the protruding bellies of the congressional team. Romário sticks to soft drinks and doesn't eat much. No sooner does he sit down than he's up on his feet again having his photo taken and signing autographs. "See that? Everyone's drinking except Romário. I spoke up for him in the Chamber; I told them he doesn't drink," remarks Chiquinho.

He was referring to an incident back in July, when Romário's car was stopped one Sunday evening in Rio, as part of a drink-driving crackdown. He refused to blow into the breathalyser, which resulted in a five-day driving suspension, a fine of R$957 and a court appearance on minor charges.

One of Romário's more than 300,000 Twitter followers tweeted: "So the law doesn't apply to those who drink, only to those who can't afford to pay the fine? You're a disgrace." Advised simply to block abusive comments, Romário wasn't going to stand back from a fight. Setting aside parliamentary decorum, the ex-footballer tweeted back: "I'll spare you my insults. Let's just say you're the disgrace – now go crawl back into your dark little hole..." He then followed it up with: "So here it is, short and sweet: say what you like and you'll end up hearing things you don't!"

Commenting on the episode, he told me: "I have the same right as any other citizen to refuse the test. That's what I did, and that's what I'll always do: exercise my rights. The press seems to think I have to take the test. I don't and I won't."

At the Lutheran University of Brazil stadium in Canoas, Romário is cheered on by 2,000 supporters. Despite his assertion that the most important thing is to focus attention on the charities he supports, he leaves the field clearly annoyed at having lost 3-2 to the Rio Grande do Sul state legislators. Nevertheless, he scored both the federal team's goals and he gets a standing ovation as he leaves the pitch. "Could you ever have imagined seeing a stadium full of thousands of people standing to applaud a bunch of politicians?" he asks, proud of his achievement.

Romário says he became "hooked" with politics the moment he realised he could do things as a congressman that he could never achieve as a football star. Besides, he likes keeping busy. "I really miss Congress," he said on a recent trip to Mexico. He spent two weeks in Guadalajara working as a commentator at the Pan-American Games. He checked the parliamentary rules before going and decided to forgo his November salary, even though he was entitled to two weeks' paid leave.

"I don't need the money: it's only twenty-six thousand reais. I could be earning much, much more. The important thing isn't how much I earn, it's what I'm doing," he says. His monthly income as a congressman (R$60,000 "office expenses" and R$3,000 accommodation allowance) is marginal compared to what he earned as a footballer.

Towards the end of 2008, Romário met Marcos Antônio Teixeira at Balada Mix, a juice bar in the upmarket Rio suburb of Barra da Tijuca. Originally from the north-eastern state of Piauí and now based in Rio, Teixeira was a member of the Brazilian Socialist Party (PSB) and had over twenty years' experience in politics. At a friend's suggestion, Teixeira tried to persuade the ex-footballer to stand for election. Romário told him he had three fears: damage to his reputation, campaign costs and defeat.

When I met Teixeira recently, at the Odeon café in the centre of Rio, he told me how, after that conversation, he commissioned a survey to assess Romário's potential as a candidate. "Popularity doesn't necessarily translate into votes, and I wanted a scientific analysis," said Teixeira, who himself studied politics at Rio de Janeiro State University.

The survey produced some surprises. The fact that Romário had a reputation for pig-headedness was viewed positively. "People saw him as someone who spoke his mind and didn't mince his words," said Teixeira. Nor did playing footvolley on the beach seem to give him a reputation for idleness. On the contrary, he was seen as a man with attitude, who made up his own mind. "The positive aspects always outweighed the negative," he said.

Alexandre Cardoso, president of the PSB in Rio, was one of the first to champion Romário's candidacy and fought hard on his behalf. "I was determined to show that he could put all these deeply held feelings to good use, helping the most disadvantaged," said Cardoso. "Romário is motivated by emotion. He does things for love."

The party saw Romário as a way of gaining popularity that didn't involve making welfare promises. "A third of the population of Greater Rio is functionally illiterate, and we need leaders who can connect us with those sections of society, the kind of places where the churches and vigilante militias operate," said Cardoso. "Romário is completely different to Tiririca; he takes the political process to the people."

Once he'd convinced himself he stood a good chance of winning, Romário accepted the challenge. His campaign began at 5:30 one morning, handing out leaflets at Rio's Central Station. "I wanted to see if he really would get up before dawn," said Teixeira. "And we also wanted to show that it was a real campaign – the workers needed to see that it wasn't just a bit of celebrity fanfare." Same time next day, in the rain, Romário was out canvassing for votes on the ferries plying across the bay between Rio and Niterói.

Many *favelas*, slums, suburbs, supermarkets and tears later, and nearly two stones heavier (with no time to exercise, he finished the campaign weighing in at over thirteen stone), Romário was elected to Congress with 146,859 votes, the sixth highest in the state of Rio de Janeiro. He appointed Marcos Antônio Teixeira as his chief of staff.

When he arrived in Brasília, Romário was allotted office 825 in the parliament building. Not only was it bigger than the others and had its own private toilet, it had been Luiz Inácio Lula da Silva's office back in 1988. Romário didn't like it: he wanted an office that ended with 11, the number he always wore on the football pitch, not the former president's. It wasn't difficult to arrange a swap with Romero Rodrigues from the PSDB, who had room 411.

The first few weeks in Congress were a frustrating time. "What am I doing here?" he often found himself wondering. "The committees hadn't yet been convened so only the Chamber itself was sitting, and the Chamber is the most boring thing in the whole place – everyone nods off, no one pays any attention to anything." At the beginning, he kept quiet and observed. "By the time I started to speak, I was on the ball: I knew who to call 'leader', who to call 'chairman', and who to call 'Your Excellency'," explains Romário, who's more used to calling everyone "boss" or "buddy".

He was appointed vice-chairman of the Tourism and Sport Committee, alternate member of the Education and Culture Committee, vice-chairman of the All-Party Group for Defending the Rights of Persons with Disabilities, and director of Accessibility and Sport at the All-Party Group for Physical Activity. In his first year, he spoke eleven times in the Chamber, compiled three reports, presented forty-eight proposals and got two amendments through, to Provisional Measure 529, relating to issues of disability. His achievements earned him sixth place in the Congress in Focus Prize, voted for by the public from a list of twenty-five congressmen nominated by press corps journalists.

"The only people who are surprised are those who don't know my ability to get what I want," he says. "There's a whole stack of congressmen who haven't got a single comma passed, even after three or four terms of office. I've got two amendments through in seven months. I'm not here just for the sake of being here; I want to make a mark, do something different."

Both of the amendments tabled by Romário were about extending the rights of people with disabilities. He asked his aides whom he needed to pester in order to get them passed. He did exactly what they suggested, explaining to the leaders of every party, in both the Chamber and the Senate, how the amendments would help thousands of disabled people. He spent hours patiently hanging around, waiting to speak to the party bigwigs, pretended to laugh at numerous football jokes and paid several visits to the Cabinet Office, the Speaker of the Chamber and the Ministry for Social Development and Hunger Eradication, in addition to conducting frequent meetings with various like-minded groups and associations, asking them also to put pressure on the government.

He got the amendments approved unanimously and was widely praised, even by the opposition. "We usually take the floor to protest at the unconstitutionality of provisional measures and vote against them, but today we're delighted to do exactly the opposite, and we declare our party's support for this provisional measure," announced Senator Álvaro Dias when it came to the vote. "I believe it is only right to highlight the role of Congressman Romário and his determination to ensure dignity for disabled persons."

Watching the Senate debate, Romário held his head in his hands and let the tears run down his face. "It was one of the most emotional moments in my life," he said later. "It was a good tortoise," he joked, showing his new familiarity with political jargon: "tortoise" amendments are the miscellaneous additions that get tacked on to this type of legislation.

"I'm always having to ask Romário to slow down," says Teixeira. "He's very motivated, he gets sent a lot of draft legislation for him to sponsor, and he gets irritated when there's too much talk and not enough action. Bit by bit, he's realising that parliament comes from *parlez*. The democratic process works in slow motion, that's just the way it is."

When the Chamber is sitting, Romário's behaviour can seem rather odd. There are days when he greets colleagues and chats jovially. On other days, he sits on his own at the back and doesn't speak to anyone. "I don't have to smile and laugh for everyone," he explains. "Some days you wake up in a good mood, sometimes you don't. I'm not being frosty; that's just the way I am."

Frosty or not, he takes his work seriously. Up until the trip to Mexico, he had a 100 per cent attendance record in the Chamber and almost the same for the Tourism and Sport Committee. As for the photos of him playing footvolley on the beach when Congress was sitting, during his very first week as a congressman, his rather irritated reply is that "people have got it all mixed up. I did nothing wrong. Yes, Congress was in session, but I'd been excused. Got it?"

He takes great care with his Portuguese. He checks spellings with his aides ("Is *lazer* with an 's' or a 'z'?") and doesn't abbreviate his text messages, making a point of writing all the words out in full. He has numerous people working on his speeches. "I read them several times, to make sure that Romário is still in there, that they haven't changed my personality," he says. "I'm a down-to-earth guy and I don't use fancy phrases."

On the bus between Porto Alegre and São Leopoldo, the day after the Canoas game, Romário is reading the Portuguese edition of *The Purpose Driven Life: What on Earth Am I Here For?* by Pastor Rick Warren. In his bag, he's also carrying *The Art of War* by Sun Tzu, with sentences underlined and notes scribbled in the margins. Encouraged by his wife ("she's a real evangelical"), he's been devoting himself to bible study for the last two years: "I've read all of it, or nearly all."

He's tired; the previous night he was out on the town with his colleagues. "I've always liked going out, and I think I'll go on liking it till I die," he says. "It's just that nowadays, I prefer to do things a little differently: calmer and not as often. I used to go out a lot; these days, once a fortnight is about right. I'm also more faithful, but if people don't want to believe that, well, that's up to them."

He was an avowed womaniser from an early age. At school, he went out with Elaine from the age of thirteen until he was eighteen, but during those five years he dated almost every other girl in the school. He lost his virginity at fourteen with Katia, while he was going out with Elaine. During the Junior World Cup in 1985, the first time he was dropped from the national team, he got caught leaning out of the window of the team's hotel in Copacabana, flirting with girls.

From then on, Romário's love life and nights out were a constant feature of the sports pages. In 1994, when playing for Barcelona, he was caught partying the night before the Champions League semi-final. "If I don't go out, I don't score goals," he announced to the Spanish press. Untameable, he wangled privileges like not having to attend morning training, and trading goals scored for days off.

Romário was born in 1966 in the Jacarezinho *favela*, part of the northern suburbs of Rio. He suffered from asthma and doctors advised his parents, Lita and Edevair, that they should take him to live somewhere else. They moved to Vila da Penha. Lita took in people's washing and ironing and, with no money to pay for transport, delivered the clean laundry on foot. Romário and his younger brother, Ronaldo, helped her. They also helped their dad, who worked in a paint shop and, at night, ran a liquor stall he'd set up in their back yard to help pay the bills. The brothers took turns every other night to sit in on the card games that went on till dawn. Then they went straight to the fruit market, where they unloaded trucks of watermelon from five till seven in the morning. From there, they went on to school.

In Marcus Vinícius Rezende de Moraes's book, *Romário*, Ronaldo tells how a guy used to wait for Romário on the way to school and beat him up. Their mum was very worried. One day, Ronaldo went with him and saw the guy, jumped on top of him and the pair of them rolled around down the street. The guy hit his head on the concrete and knocked himself unconscious. "From then on I took my brother to school, and even started taking my dad's .22 revolver with me," Ronaldo says in the book. "It left a deep mark on Romário, and for a long time afterwards he kept having dreams about the beatings."

When they weren't working or up to no good (like stealing chickens to supplement their lunch), Romário and Ronaldo played football. As the boys' reward for getting through their end-of-year school exams, Edevair put together a neighbourhood football team, called

Estrelinha. From Estrelinha, Romário went on to play for Olaria, and from there on to Vasco. He had spells at Flamengo, Fluminense and America, while abroad he played for PSV in Holland, and Barcelona and Valencia in Spain. There followed a brief but highly lucrative stay at Al-Sadd in Qatar. After that, playing for Miami FC in the USA and Adelaide United in Australia helped him reach the milestone of scoring 1,000 goals. Wherever he went, controversy followed.

He retired from playing in 2008. Off the pitch, he tried his hand at being a coach for Vasco, then a businessman, before deciding to run for Congress. "I was a footballer, but I wasn't an athlete. Now I'm a congressman, but I'm not a politician," he explains. "I don't want a career in politics. I'm giving it everything I've got for this term of office. After that, I'll stop."

When asked if it wasn't contradictory to say he'd stop in 2014, while still putting his name forward to be PSB candidate for mayor of Rio at the next election, he replies: "Look, all terms of office last four years. Let's suppose the opportunity to run for mayor comes up: instead of stopping in 2015, I'd be stopping in 2016. Two years, give or take, hardly makes any difference. Right?"

In reality he was very enthusiastic at the prospect of standing for mayor. However, Alexandre Cardoso poured cold water on the idea, declaring that the PSB would support Eduardo Paes's re-election. "It didn't bother me. I understand that the party already had its strategy in place," says Romário.

For the entire thirty-odd miles from Porto Alegre to São Leopoldo, Romário sits with his arms folded and his hands tucked under his armpits, his legs fidgeting restlessly. As they arrive, the other congressmen call out: "Romário! Open the curtain – people want to see you!"

Before getting off the bus, Romário fires his parting shot: "Jérôme is coming to Congress on Tuesday, and I'm going to give him a thrashing he'll never forget. He said that no one, not Romário nor any other congressman, could beat FIFA. Well, I'm going to put him and Ricardo Teixeira in their places."

Afterwards he explains to me: "It's a complete joke what they're up to. It's a question of sovereignty: we're the people, these are our laws. So it's not what FIFA wants? Tough. It's federal, goddam it. This is my fight, my battle." He assures me he isn't still bitter about 2002, when Ricardo Teixeira, chairman of the Brazilian Football Federation (CBF), went back on a promise to pick him for the World Cup. On Sunday Romário leaves the match at half-time to catch his flight back to Rio. At six a.m. the next morning, he's on another flight, this time to get him to the São Paulo state legislative assembly by nine a.m. São Paulo is the last of the twelve host cities to be inspected by the 2014 World Cup Legislative Forum, which oversees the tournament. They follow the same routine in every city: first of all a meeting with the local legislative assembly, then a lunch with the governor and mayor, and finally a visit to the construction sites at the stadiums and airports.

Romário's assessment of the whole thing: "On PowerPoint everything looks amazing. I know exactly what's going to happen – they'll dress everything up for when we visit. But some of the stadiums aren't going to be ready in time." Wherever he goes, he talks about the excessive expenditure and the lack of an enduring social legacy.

On Tuesday, November 8, the public hearing with Ricardo Teixeira and Jérôme Valcke, general secretary of FIFA, is scheduled to start at 9:00. Teixeira and Valcke arrive an hour later, accompanied by Marco Maia. Romário arrives at 10:30, holding a piece of paper with seven questions. With him is Afonso Morais, a PSB sports journalist. "Romário wants everything written down," explains Morais. "He absorbs it all quickly, knows all the details and challenges everything they tell him. I never imagined he would be so thorough."

While still in Guadalajara, Romário heard that the request for a public hearing had been granted. He called Morais and said to him: "I know what they're like, and the public have the right to know too. We have to show them who the Brazilian government is getting into bed with." Together the two of them drew up a list of questions to ask the football barons.

Romário's opening line has not been prepared, and comes as a surprise to Morais: "I have no particular or personal interest in getting into a fight with FIFA. As an elected congressman, I have the democratic legitimacy to be sitting here, unlike the gentleman opposite. I'm going to fight tooth and nail to stop FIFA building a state within this state."

Romário goes on to claim that he's holding in his hand a letter in which Sepp Blatter, the FIFA president, had apparently made some derogatory comments about Valcke. Two years after that letter was written, continued Romário, Valcke had been hired as FIFA's marketing director, but had then, it was claimed, been sacked when FIFA switched their global sponsor from MasterCard to Visa. Six months later, Valcke was rehired, this time as general secretary. Reading from his piece of paper, his legs fidgeting again, Romário comes to his first question: "Is there some reason Joseph Blatter is afraid of you?"

Just as he's starting his second question, Congressman Renan Filho signals that his three minutes are already up. Romário gets annoyed. "I'm not finished yet!" he erupts, and turns to Ricardo Teixeira. "You promised that building the World Cup stadiums would be financed by private money. That's not, unfortunately, what we're seeing now, with grants from the federal government. What happened? Was there no coordination between the CBF, FIFA, the Ministry of Sport and the Local Organising Committee, which you also chair?"

Romário is interrupted by Renan Filho once again, but carries on: "Can I make one final point? I don't receive money from FIFA or any of the World Cup sponsors." He starts talking about the "football lobby", those legislators who receive campaign funding from the football bosses, when he is yet again interrupted.

Before handing over to Ricardo Teixeira, Renan Filho notes for the record that, in accordance with the rules of the committee, witnesses are only required to answer questions relating directly to the World Cup General Law.

The next day Romário agrees to help write a letter to the Swiss government, asking it to make public its investigations into FIFA. The request is to be delivered by hand to the Minister of Justice, Eduardo Cardozo. "There were only downsides for me going into politics, and yet today I am respected by the other congressmen as an effective politician," he tells me. "I feel more and more at home in politics – I don't know whether that's a good or a bad thing."

On December 16, Romário goes to the World Cup Local Organising Committee in Rio to meet Ricardo Teixeira and Ronaldo Luís Nazário de Lima, Romário's one-time strike partner, who's recently been appointed to the LOC's board of directors. He's accepted their invitation, Romário says, because he wants to understand how Ronaldo fits into the LOC set-up. A few days earlier, Romário had warned Ronaldo that he should carry out his own audit of the organisation, in order to protect himself against any irregularities that might have occurred before his appointment. The meeting is presented in the press as a reconciliation between Romário and Ricardo Teixeira. Romário does, in fact, come out of the meeting smiling, saying he'll soon be announcing another victory for the interests of disabled people. He insists, however, that he hasn't buried the hatchet with Teixeira: "The good guys won't be disappointed."

Juan Pablo Meneses. Santiago de Chile, 1969. Writer and journalist. He is the author of several books, including *Equipaje de mano* (2003), *La vida de una vaca* (2008) and *Niños futbolistas* (2013). He studied journalism in Santiago and in Barcelona. In Mexico he edited *Generación ¡Bang!* (2012), an anthology of young narco-*crónica* writers, while in Buenos Aires he founded the Portable Journalism School (Escuela de Periodismo Portátil). He currently lives in Chile, where he is the editor of the daily *hoyxhoy* and teaches at Universidad de Chile.

'A Grenade for River Plate' ('*Una granada para River Plate*') was first published in *Equipaje de mano* in 2003.

A GRENADE FOR RIVER PLATE

Juan Pablo Meneses

Translated by Jethro Soutar

El Polaco appears brandishing his Stanley, as he lovingly calls his pocket knife. Five young hooligans huddle round him like classroom students. He leaves them gobsmacked with a dazzling display of knife skills: in under a minute, he unscrews the four bolts in the reading light and air-vent panel over seats 31 and 32. Much to the consternation (or cowardice, according to El Polaco) of those travelling with the *barra* for the first time, he then removes the casing from the roof, leaving everything exposed, everything being the jumble of wires and cables that are usually hidden from public view. Hidden and forgotten about, which is how the *barra* feel they're treated by society.

"Before we hide it, we have to wrap it up in something... We need a hat," El Polaco says, and one of his disciples snatches a cap off a younger *barra*'s head.

"Everyone has to muck in here, *compadre*," the timid young lad is told, as he watches his blue cap, red "U" embroidered on the front, disappear into a sea of twenty-year-old hands.

El Polaco carefully wraps the grenade up in the cap. That's right, the grenade. A weapon of war. We have a miniature bomb on the bus with us. A genuine piece of munition that someone stole, we're told, from the army when doing military service.

"They're amazingly easy to launch. You just pull this pin, release the safety catch with your teeth and chuck it," one of the more experienced *barra* adds calmly. Fear paralyses the rest of us: football fans who've left behind parents and girlfriends, neighbourhood friends, younger brothers, team posters on bedroom walls, a flag commemorating last year's league title, a collection of match tickets in the bedside drawer. All left behind, at home, a place that seems increasingly far away. All to go on an away trip abroad for the first time. All for the team.

With the speed and dexterity of a practised pickpocket, El Polaco tucks the hat-explosive in among the cables and screws the panel back in place. He leaves not a trace. Nothing to suggest that above the reading lights of seats 31 and 32 is a bomb.

"There's no fucking way customs'll find it," he says, putting his Stanley back in its secret pocket.

But peace refuses to return to the Chilebus, packed with travelling football supporters: just when we think the worst is over, something leaps out and grabs us by the throat:

"So which one of you fuckers is going to throw it then?"

The question – in your face, pure adrenalin – is fired at us by one of the *barra*'s leaders. There are members of "the firm"'s hierarchy on all the buses. They tell us what to do and report back to the high command. This one continues:

"Time to sort out the men from the boys, find out which one of you fuckers is the hardest. Who's got the balls to take the grenade into the ground and throw it. Or are we all a bunch of fucking pussies in this *barra*?"

The business of who will launch the explosive is thankfully left unresolved. There are no initial volunteers. For now, the order of the day is to celebrate the fact that the piece of infantry equipment has been safely concealed. A bottle of *pisco* is passed around, followed by a carton of red wine and several spliffs. Normality is suddenly restored. The bus goes back to being a vehicle taking a group of football supporters to Buenos Aires: chants break out deriding River Plate fans – *gallinas*; banter flies back and forth, accusing people of holding on to the wine for too long, of hogging the spliff. Practically the whole bus ends up joining in with the songs.

The leader of our bus is San Martín: hacking cough, hands covered in scars, sunglasses, a walk that's more of a shoulder barge, and too much jewellery for the circumstances. He tells us in a paternal tone – albeit that of a father who beats his son – that we're going to war.

"If we have to die for the team in Argentina, then that's what we'll do. I don't want to see any pussies wimping out. We stand united."

Someone goes up to the front of the bus and persuades the driver to put on a tape: Rage Against the Machine. For a while the sound of the US metal band takes hold of the Chilebus. A *barra* wearing a Che Guevara T-shirt rocks his head to the beat of the Yankee drummer. Outside the bus, the Santiago outskirts pass by: dirt football pitches, kids on street corners, stray dogs comatose in the sun. Inside the bus the music gets faster and louder, as does the passing round of bottles, a never-ending supply of wine and *pisco*, multiplying as if for our last supper. We're going on a trip. We're going to see a football match. We're going to Buenos Aires, with a hand grenade inches above our heads.

The explosive is like any trauma: you forget about it for a while, but it never goes away. JG, the photographer travelling with me, looks at me with bloodshot eyes and whispers:

"If they find out we're here doing a story, we're dead."

Our bus is Bus Three of eleven that set off from "La U" headquarters, or *Corporación de Fútbol de la Universidad de Chile*, as the team is officially known. We're not on the bus with the really big fishes, the heads of the firm, but nor are we at the back of the caravan with the minnows, the least experienced. We're going to the Argentine capital to cheer the team on in the semi-final of the Copa Libertadores. We're going to get one over on the River Plate *gallinas*, and in their own back yard.

"We're going to die!" someone shouts, and then gobs on the floor.

We're travelling with Los de Abajo, the worst hooligans in Chile.

In the first leg of the semi-final, played in Santiago, a minor incident involving a few River Plate fans and the local police was blown out of all proportion. The sporting press exaggerated the extent of the confrontation until it snowballed into a gigantic chauvinistic scandal, worthy of the intervention of both countries' foreign ministers. All of which means the Chilean newspapers have been warning of one thing all week: that hell awaits us in Buenos Aires.

There are thirty-eight men on the bus, two women, and two pens: JG's and mine. For a moment, we worry this might give the game away. We're saved by the panic to fill in customs and immigration forms, for in the mad rush the source of the pens gets overlooked.

"You have to fill in these papers in order to leave the country," says the bus driver's assistant, who everyone has started calling "The Man".

We're half an hour away from Paso Los Libertadores, the main border crossing between Chile and Argentina, when The Man hands out the forms. Trying to get forty sets of forms filled in with only two pens, while being asked the same question a hundred times and subjected to endless piss-taking, proves too much for The Man. He looks exasperated when he's finished, at the end of his tether. His Chilebus company tie and cap still speak of a kindly travel assistant, but his brusque manners, his waspish attitude and the thunderous look on his face are the outward signs of an internal crisis: for the first time ever, he seems to be seriously thinking about quitting his job, a job he's had his whole life.

We're three hours into a trip that will last a minimum of sixty.

We reach the Chilean side. A tourist couple in a car take photos of the football supporters in their blue shirts. We pass quickly through immigration while customs officials take just over an hour to search the eleven buses. Neither process goes without a hitch: from our bus alone, three people are unable to travel any further: one because his ID card has expired, one because he didn't bring any ID at all, and San Martín, our leader, because his ID card is what everyone calls "dirty": he has a number of pending court cases and a restriction order to his name.

We enter the tunnel that separates the two countries. A sign goes past the window that says *"Bienvenido a Argentina"*, bringing the sudden realisation that there's no easy way back from this journey.

"We've left…" JG whispers to me, but before he's finished what he has to say, a fat joint is pressed into his hand, to see us through to the next stage of the border crossing.

There's an immediate change of attitude on the Argentinian side. The hellish treatment promised by the press starts to become real.

"Their police are bad to the bone," a friend warned me before the trip. "Thirty thousand Argentines died under their dictatorship, that's a lot more than under Pinochet."

On a routine crossing, formalities at the border rarely take more than half an hour. After five hours have passed and we still haven't got through customs, rumours start to circulate. Someone says the sniffer dogs have detected a shipment of marijuana. Never mind the speculation, all I can think of is the grenade, which I know is real, for I've seen it with my own eyes, practically had to touch it. But our bus passes safely through, and I find this strangely comforting: El Polaco didn't let us down, which is why we all pat him on the back as he walks by, full of smiles, asking to cadge a fag off someone.

The Argentine border police have forbidden any of the buses from leaving until every vehicle has been searched. At some point in the delay, some of the *barra* start singing the Chilean national anthem. There are Argentine flags everywhere, hanging from garage flagpoles and stuck to office windows, alongside posters of President Menem and his party. We get to the end of the first verse, singing at the tops of our voices in protest against the way we're being treated, when a border patrol agent comes out of a reinforced door. He has a moustache like Videla's, and a sub-machine gun.

"No fucking singing!" he screams.

It starts to get dark. Mendoza passers-by greet us with raised middle fingers, by placing hands on crotches and running index fingers across necks. You have to be mentally prepared for a journey like this, where violence is ever present. For some of us, the hostility we encounter whenever we get off the bus is a new experience. For others, the majority, it's routine, something they've been used to since childhood, and without which they'd feel lost.

In the outskirts of Mendoza we're detained again. While we're waiting, the new leader of the bus passes a hat around, in case anyone would "like to chip in with a few pennies", as he jovially puts it, though it's clearly an order rather than an option. We're essentially forced to empty our pockets into the makeshift collection box, and when the leaders have raised sufficient funds, they disappear.

They come back forty minutes later, laden with wine and beer. Just after midnight, after more than fourteen hours on the road, the caravan restarts its journey to Buenos Aires.

A group of police patrol cars accompanies us as far as the city limits, sirens blaring, officers hanging out of open windows. Inside the bus, toasts are made, there's shouting, music and smoke. Outside the bus there are mean faces, rifles pointed at our heads.

The night brings calm. On the bus, "The House" as it's been christened by the group, the cold is kept at bay by denim jackets, cartons of Mendoza wine, bottles of beer, marijuana, chocolate and cigarettes. *Young Guns* I and II play on the Chilebus television screen. Protests at the poor quality of the entertainment on offer only abate whenever there's a knife fight.

Some people – those in the seats nearest to the driver – are already asleep. Others put headphones on and listen to Walkmans, resting heads against windows and watching the white lines of the motorway go by, perhaps thinking about what lies in store or what we've already been through; about the relentless police aggression, the way we're treated as dangers to the public; about the music thundering in our ears, the giant stars hanging in the pampas sky; about blue woolly hats on our heads, a present from a girlfriend, or the warmth of team shirts under jackets.

The Man appears at the back of The House, carrying a pillow. He has cotton buds in his ears and a tired look on his face, a look that would easily get to the final of a South American tired-faces tournament. A hatch suddenly opens by the toilet, revealing a secret compartment. The Man climbs in and curls up like a foetus, ready to get some sleep. He barely says a word, but he's visibly furious. He's angry because this is no regular run to Buenos Aires, and because even on regular runs, his bedroom is a narrow metal coffin over a Chilebus toilet, a coffin he enters alive.

"My brother lives in Buenos Aires. Motherfucker's lived there for years," El Polaco tells a small gathering by the toilet. "He's an international gangster, know what I mean? Motherfucker's made it big."

Someone else chimes in:

"Son of a bitch, I've an aunty in Buenos Aires – I didn't even think to bring her address. Apparently she works in some millionaire's house," he says, before tipping back the wine box.

"We've got to fucking win tomorrow," says Jorge, changing the subject. Jorge has taken two days' leave from the printers where he works. "It's the first time we've ever got this close to the final."

The first predictions come in.

127

"Two-nil us. One from Marcelito Salas, the other from Huevo Valencia," says Citroneta, a biology student from Valparaíso University, who's been naively trying to pass himself off as a bad boy.

Jorge is in his thirties, same as the friend he's come with. His friend says:

"It's amazing to think we might reach the Copa Libertadores final, when you think back to the bad old days, going to the ground and knowing we'd lose."

"Son of a bitch, it was like that for fucking years! When we went down to the second division we were always going on trips like this, though there was less aggro of course. You lot'll never experience any of that. You guys have it easy, with the team winning all the time."

The vehicle gently rocks from side to side, though with all the wine and weed, it seems to rock that little bit more. The Man pokes his head out of his secret compartment and yells for people to let him get some sleep. A hand reaches round and slaps him in the face, whose hand it's impossible to say. Los de Abajo's hand.

Morning breaks at six. The sun pokes out over the prairie like the flicker of a brain-dead eye. Most people contemplate the landscape in silence. The windows are steamed up – you have to wipe them with a sleeve to see out. Drops of condensation run startled down the glass as the endless plains of the Argentine pampas open up before us. Someone sparks up the first spliff of the day. The smoking's not raucous now: it's more like background music, the strumming of an acoustic guitar. We wake up slowly, on our way to Buenos Aires.

By general petition – "we've got to piss and splash some fucking water on our face, man" – we stop at a Repsol service station. The little shop is overrun by football supporters. JG, who has been snapping away, pretending to be a student who takes photos as a hobby, nudges for me to look. Here they come, swarming back to the bus, great bulges under their coats. People did go to the loo and wash their faces, but the main purpose of the stop-off was to loot the Argentinian store.

As we speed away, The Man and the driver say out loud how such behaviour makes them ashamed to be Chilean. Through the bus window we see the salesgirl talking to someone on the phone, presumably the police, her head bowed, her weak fist pounding the plundered counter.

Once we're back on the motorway, Citroneta, the university student with the long hair and John Lennon glasses, gets out his booty, excited that he's finally about to be accepted by the group.

"Anyone want some wine?" he says, and produces a carton of red from the depths of his jacket. Behind him another haul is unveiled: a litre of gin, a bundle of pens ("so we never run out of these bastards again") and a bottle of perfume ("now the missus will let me shag her for weeks without any dramas").

Citroneta goes quiet, lost for words, crestfallen. Someone opens a bottle of whisky. Someone else opens a box of cigars.

"I told you, Argentina's ridiculously cheap," says El Polaco, before he takes a deep tug on his Havana and almost punctures a lung. We all splutter with laughter, laughter that tastes of Scotch.

The next stop is Luján, forty miles outside the capital. It's eleven o'clock on match-day morning, though by now time seems as irrelevant as La U's starting line-up. We're surrounded by police again. For a joke, a sergeant pulls his gun on the group I'm standing in: he motions as if he's going to shoot and laughs his head off when we throw ourselves to the ground. Someone produces a football, and a fat guy from Bus Seven plays commentator, describing in a grizzly voice the goal that Marcelo Salas is going to score to take us into the Copa Libertadores final.

"Back on the bus you bunch of fuckwits, we're off!" shouts El Polaco, leaning out of the bus door, proudly showing off the sunglasses he stole at the service station.

"I can't believe you fell for that fake shit," says Jorge, the print worker.

"Fake? You off your fucking rocker? They're Bollé originals. Look, it says Bollé right here!" El Polaco takes off his shades to show us all. "I wouldn't have robbed the fuckers otherwise, would I?"

The Buenos Aires clocks strike three in the afternoon as a column of buses bearing La U and Chile flags enters the city. The match will kick off in a few hours' time and nationalist insults fly back and forth between Los de Abajo and local passers-by.

As our caravan crosses Avenida General Paz, we're stopped by the Policía General Argentina. A full brigade of riot police has been waiting for us, with all the humanity of a metal detector. Out of the window we see two blue armoured cars, a riot van and three patrol cars; all have their sirens blaring. A television crew wearing PFA (Policía Federal de Argentina) jackets and military boots gathers footage of every bus, a swirl of cameras and police helmets bobbing up and down outside. The whole ceremony lasts for over an hour, and as we're ordered to keep the windows closed, the combination of the heat, the lack of air and the smell of the detritus on the bus starts to become asphyxiating. While we wait for permission to move on, El Polaco taunts a couple of policemen, opening a window at the back of the bus and throwing an empty beer bottle at the camera.

"That's how you provoke them, dipshit. There's no need to ask for it," says Citroneta, who like many people has taken off his shirt to mop up his sweat.

The Man, in the cabin up front with the driver, dressed in his immaculate shirt and tie, shakes his head from side to side, cursing the day his boss told him he was to take Los de Abajo to Buenos Aires. Worse still: cursing his life, cursing his job and his future.

We're given the order to advance, which marks the start of a strange tour of Buenos Aires, with two armour-plated anti-riot vans for guides. It's the first time many of the *barra* have been outside Chile. They glue their faces to the windows and make the most of the opportunity to get to know the city that has produced the most fearsome and legendary *barras bravas* on the continent. A city whose hooligan firms, like so many things in Argentina, are inspired by the English. The capital city of a country where 9.5 fans die on average every year due to football violence. A country where most firms rely on the direct support of political bigwigs, who employ them to go on marches, to administer beatings, to wave banners, and to cheer the team on every Sunday. But we can only sample the most important city in the Southern Cone, only taste the quaint European pretensions of its citizens, from on board the Chilebus: due to orders from above, we're not allowed to get off.

Instructions have come in from Bus Two, on which the Los de Abajo inner council are travelling, that the only permitted stop-off will be in La Boca. The plan is to join up with members of La 12, Boca Juniors' *barra brava*, who are going to "borrow our clothes", that's to say, help us fight against their eternal rivals, River Plate.

We get off the bus down by the waterfront. According to official communications, we're to meet back in the same place in half an hour. But as we make our collective way up Calle Caminito, waving blue flags and shouting "La U", some members of the *barra* scrawl graffiti on the multi-coloured walls, sullying the neighbourhood's iconic architecture with the words "Los de Abajo". And so the trouble begins. Those members of La 12 who live in La Boca see the graffiti as an affront and quickly get organised: soon the supposed *barra* brothers of La U and Boca Juniors, who were meant to unite against one common enemy, are fighting among themselves. The street brawl that follows results in various injuries and thefts, and includes the loss of numerous flags through abandonment and confiscation. Several La U fans are mugged and lose wallets, while a guy from Bus Five is also relieved of his shirt, his watch, his cigarettes and his penknife.

The police act like referees at a boxing match, albeit referees only interested in penalising Chilean blows below the belt.

"Boca folk don't have friends," a sergeant snarls through gritted teeth, as he leads a member of Bus Four away in handcuffs.

La Boca is in uproar: fat old ladies demand the Chileans be thrown in jail; poor kids dressed in Maradona T-shirts spit out insults.

"The bus is family!" our leader cries when we're all safely back on board. "A little scuffle with a few Boca sons of bitches and look what happens! Tonight we're going to be up against 70,000 *gallinas*. We've got to stick together. The bus is family!"

Jorge, from the printing firm, tried to make the most of the pit stop by going off to buy souvenirs for his work colleagues. He gets back to the bus with his head split open, blood pouring down his face. Finding himself all alone, he was pounced on and took a beating. He now sits sprawled out in his seat, wishing he were back at the office. El Polaco offers him his T-shirt to wipe the blood up and Jorge wraps it round his head like a turban. For many passengers, the threat of finding hell in Buenos Aires has become a reality.

Off we go again, our caravan of eleven buses, leaving La Boca behind and making for the stadium. One of our number has a bleeding head, several others have been mugged and/or threatened with knives, two have been arrested – though they'll later be released – and everywhere we've been the police have flocked to us like flies to shit. Off we go again, bound for the stadium, and I haven't forgotten we've got a hand grenade on board.

Our last port of call before the stadium is Avenida Figueroa Alcorta, across from the airport. The caravan parks along one side of the road, and a few *barra* fling themselves on a grass bank to rest. Others nurse their wounds, smoke a final spliff or swig the last of the beer. Walter, the queen bee, leader of the supporters' club and head honcho of the *barra*, shows himself for the first time.

He's the most formally dressed of all of us. He looks more like a McDonald's employee of the month, a cool teacher at an IT training college or the local church's guitar player than he does the head of a hooligan firm. His hair is neatly combed, his shirt is tucked inside his trousers, his trainers are pristine white – they've obviously never kicked a football. It's possible Walter never even dreamt of being a footballer: he perhaps fantasised about becoming a club director, treasurer or chairman. But somehow he's ended up in charge of the toughest *barra* in Chile, and as leader of the supporters' club he gets to interact with the club management. Maybe it was the only way for him to follow his dreams.

Walter wanders through the crowd, appealing for calm, saying that the tickets are on their way, reminding everyone to be careful and alert to provocations later on.

"It's all sorted," he says, "a club director left on a flight out of Santiago three hours ago and is meeting us here with the tickets."

On average we've paid the equivalent of US$70 each for the trip, for travel and a ticket to the game.

"But only the newcomers pay that much," El Polaco tells me, adding that he travels for free because he spent two months passing the firm's collection pot round at home matches.

The directors of the *barra* don't pay anything either, while those lower down the pecking order pay half, or whatever they can afford.

The first cars of River Plate fans pass along Figueroa Alcorta on their way to the ground. They hurl abuse at us, sound their horns, shout, "Die starving Chileans," but we haven't the energy to respond. The print worker, El Polaco's shirt still tied round his head, tells his horror story to passengers from Bus Six. A member of Bus Eight shows everyone the knife slashes in his forearm. The voice of someone clearly still in shock proclaims that we're all going to be savaged by 70,000 *gallinas*. A long silence follows. JG puts his camera away and lies back on the grass, experiencing the historic moment through nothing but his own fear.

Walter, our supreme leader, disappears up the road in a taxi. Half an hour passes. Finally he returns with a full batch of tickets. He seems happy at having hobnobbed with the club directors in their five-star hotel and maybe a little sad to be back among such a band of ruffians.

He hands out the tickets, one by one, telling people to keep cool, to try and relax. El Pelluco, El Krammer, El Traitor, El Jhonny and El Mono, other legends of the *barra*, help him in the distribution. The time has finally come to go to the ground.

The hordes are drawn like moths to the bright floodlights of River's Estadio Monumental. We'll soon be inside the ground, hoping La U can reach the Copa Libertadores final for the first time. We're ready to give it our all, to lay our lives on the line, to beat the bloody Argies in an important game for once.

As our caravan of buses approaches the Estadio Monumental, the mass of River fans outside gets thicker and thicker. For every yard we advance, the crowd grows tenfold. Our movement becomes increasingly sporadic, until we flounder like an overturned beetle. The Man decides to switch off the lights inside the bus. Outside, the anti-Chile chanting can be heard loud and clear, too clear. We struggle to make any progress at all, run aground in a sea of white shirts with red sashes.

The River supporters we've been trying to weave our way through start rocking the bus, trying to turn it over. There are now thousands and thousands of them out there. Our leader shouts for us to draw the curtains and duck down behind the seats, then the windows of The House start to shatter, one after another, as rocks ricochet down the passageway. Lying on the floor, broken windows above our heads, the cries of the *gallinas* echo in our ears like the roar of a lion moving in on its prey. El Polaco sighs, takes a deep breath, opens a window and shouts, "Argentinian motherfuckers!" and hurls out two large empty beer bottles. And again: "Argentinian cunts!" followed by two more bottles. He ducks back down and a rock explodes against the side of the bus, right where his head had been. The insults are now coming from very close quarters, but we can also make out the sound of spurs on mounted police. Finally they step in and escort us to the ground.

Kick-off is only minutes away.

The stadium is packed. The police have held us on the stairway leading into the Centenario and Belgrano blocks. We're awaiting an order from on high that is slow in coming. When it finally arrives, the police shove us forward by striking us with their truncheons. We enter the inner sanctum of the Estadio Monumental, coming out into the middle of the stand, an insignificant speck among 70,000 fans who pay us not the least bit of attention. The police, though, continue to lay into us, as they herd us forward. Los de Abajo spontaneously start singing, at the tops of their voices and full of rage: "Argentinian pussies, lost the Falklands cause they're wusses!"

When La U take to the field, all eleven players run over towards us and raise their hands. We respond to their gestures with chants that, paradoxically, are practically identical to the ones the River fans are singing. All twenty-two players are now on the pitch, twenty-two South American millionaires, almost all of them from the same poor neighbourhoods as the *barras*.

The match itself is like a giant vacuum. Most of the 70,000-strong crowd watch the game without getting out of their seats. Sometimes it even seems you can hear the players insulting one another down on the pitch. "The fuckers don't sing at all!" says Citroneta, feeling disorientated and cheated, wondering whether all the talk he's heard down the years of Argentina's notorious *barras bravas* being the maddest and baddest on the continent was maybe just Argentina's notorious love of talking the talk.

But we've come all this way to take them on and Los de Abajo's ringleaders are neither disheartened nor intimidated. They ask us, will us, urge us, to sing our hearts out and silence the stadium. The Monumental goes on watching the game in a giant hush and doesn't even notice us. At least not until the end of the match, when the game's over and they've won and suddenly they find their voice.

We lose one-nil. We're denied a blatant penalty for a foul on Valencia, and Silvani, our Argentine striker, misses an absolute sitter. We're out of the Copa Libertadores; the dream is over. All we can do is watch as swathes of Argentinians laugh in our faces and celebrate victory over a Chilean team for the umpteenth time.

As soon as the final whistle blows, it's announced over the loud-speaker that the home fans must stay in their seats while the visiting fans leave. We start to file out. Not even four minutes have passed since the end of the game – less than four minutes to digest defeat – when the police pile into us and start swinging their truncheons. The blows are relentless, indiscriminate and totally without provocation. Plain-clothes officers appear on the scene, many of them sporting long hair, and kick the wounded as they lie on the ground. Guns are brandished. Truncheons are aimed at elbows, to demobilise your whole arm, but there's no time even to flinch, you have to keep moving, or you might fall. If you fall, you have to cover your head straight away and protect it from being stamped on, and you might see, as I do, an unconscious policeman being carried away. "Throw the grenade!" I hear someone cry. We're underneath the stands, in the toilet area, getting a brutal police beating. But if they launch the grenade, we'll be skinned alive in a Buenos Aires jail. I'm scared. I'm stuck in a whirlwind of truncheons and shouting and pushing and shoving and swearing and shrieking and being kicked from behind and dogs barking and River fans roaring from the other side of the fence and helmets charging into us, and it's difficult to know what the hell's going on or what the hell to do, other than to keep your head down and keep going, onwards, to get this thing over and done with, as quickly as possible.

Respite comes only when the police realise that television cameras have arrived and are filming them. Final score: four fans with head wounds, one with a bloodied eye, a policeman with a broken nose and two fans under arrest (though they're let go once everything has cooled down).

As ever, a sizeable police contingent accompanies us out of the city. The ramshackle caravan crosses the pampas at night: the windows on the buses are now all broken and the pampas air rushes in at us, insufferably cold. The fresh air does at least hide the festering smell, and besides, the cold is nothing compared to the violence we've just been subjected to.

We're back at the Paso Los Libertadores border crossing, with the peaks of the Andes hidden in dark cloud. The Argentine border patrol don't even bother to stop us to check our papers: they want us out of their country as soon as possible. As we enter the tunnel, the bus breaks out in spontaneous applause. The Man sounds the horn. We're in Chile. The immigration staff welcome us home like heroes, a show of raised hands and thumbs. Two policemen get out of a car to come and shake our hands. The whole country has heard about the police beating we suffered on our way out of the stadium and our return to Chile is being hailed as triumphant. Never mind the fact that we lost: we've come back as winners. Three television channels, several radio stations and a big round of applause from customs officials lift Los de Abajo's spirits no end. We're the main news item of the day.

"Come here, you fags... Mind if I have my photo taken with you?" asks El Polaco. He's refused to be photographed the whole trip, and now suddenly *he* asks *us* for a photo. And in a nice voice too.

After the photo's been taken, he tells us it's been an unforgettable trip. Everyone laughs, thinking he's taking the piss. What nobody suspects, not even for a moment, is that in a few months' time, Walter, the leader of the *barra*, will be diagnosed with a serious medical condition, on account of all the blows he took to the head in the Estadio Monumental. Much less that he'll die from it a few years later. Nor does anyone suspect it will be El Krammer who takes control of the *barra*, and that in no time at all he'll have divided the group and be accused of profiting financially from Los de Abajo, and then be arrested for hitting the female owner of a shop in an incident captured on CCTV, and then be arrested again, this time for disfiguring the face of a rival fan, and then finally be put behind bars as the ringleader of a gang wanted for a number of armed robberies in the Santiago area. Nobody suspects that after this trip to Buenos Aires La U will fail to get beyond the first round of the Copa Libertadores for several years. Nor that the journey we've just been on will go down as the most memorable away trip in supporters' club history.

On board the bus, the future doesn't exist. All that matters is the here and now, hence the laughter when The Man says once again:

"It's been an epic journey, lads, truly epic."

This prompts another round of applause, as ridiculous at it might sound. In fact, applause rings out across Chile. And on the bus we feel proud, happy, brave – heroic like never before.

When we get off the Chilebus in Santiago, El Polaco looks sad for the first time. He asks for our phone numbers and says we should all meet up the next day, and he tells JG to take his photo, as if he knew all along that we were doing a report on the trip, on them. The buses start to leave and there are hugs all round, because of what we've been through, or achieved, and because it's all over. When The House is empty, the driver pulls away, relieved, breathing in the tranquillity of no longer having a bunch of football hooligans on his bus. Of course, what he doesn't know – not he, and not The Man – is that there's a hand grenade on board.

Wilmer Urrelo Zárate. Bolivia, 1975. He is the author of three novels: *Mundo negro* (Nuevo Milenio, 2000), winner of the National Prize for Best Debut Novel and published in Italian by Edizione Estemporanee; *Fantasmas asesinos* (Alfaguara, 2006), winner of the National Prize for Best Novel; *Hablar con los perros* (Alfaguara, 2011), winner of the Anna Seghers Prize for Literature 2012, as chosen by the Anna Seghers Foundation in Berlin, Germany. His short stories have appeared in numerous Bolivian and international anthologies.

'Lucha Libre versus Football' ('*Lucha Libre versus fútbol*') was first published on the website www.ecdotica.com in February 2010.

LUCHA LIBRE
VERSUS FOOTBALL

Wilmer Urrelo Zárate

Translated by Jethro Soutar

Before we go any further, I ought to come clean: I don't like football. I find it the most idiotic of sports, never mind the fact that as an international mafia it puts anything in Roberto Saviano's *Gomorrah* to shame. And yet – or perhaps therefore – football moves in mysterious ways, and I couldn't help but fall under its influence a few weeks ago, when I fell hostage to the fortunes of Liga de Quito. There were two simple reasons: (1) I was in Ecuador and La Liga were playing at home; (2) La Liga were playing against Fluminense, a team of Brazilians, and if there's anything worse than football it's the combination of Brazilians and football (they always win), as well as maybe Brazilians and carnival (they get to parade about with no clothes on).

Anyway, on the night La Liga played Fluminense for some cup or other – I forget which (though it was named after a car manufacturer, I do remember that) – I was leaving the Quito book fair with two distinguished colleagues: Naief Yehya from Mexico and Miguel Ángel Oxlaj from Guatemala.

We were walking through the Quito streets (so very similar to our streets back in La Paz) and you could already sense the tension: the streets were half empty, presumably because everyone was in front of a telly somewhere, either at home or in some bar. And so we walked back to the hotel, chatting about many things (cinema, books, writers – male and female – from our respective countries), and I tried hard to prevent the conversation from getting on to "that sport" (and I say "that sport" the same way we might say "that woman" in my country, conjuring up images of awful mothers-in-law and so forth). We had time to kill and we were hungry, and so we went to Sal y Pimienta, a buffet restaurant next to the hotel that served proper local food. They said they were closing at eight, and I think it was Naief who asked if it was because of the game. The girl serving us said no, then added dejectedly:

"La Liga are losing."

Wham! The first blow, below the belt. It turned out she was a big La Liga fan, but for reasons I didn't quite understand there was no TV in the restaurant, so she couldn't watch the game. But the absence of the game was there, which is basically the same thing as having it right there in front of you, rammed down your throat. And I indulged in some cod philosophy: I thought about the tension in the air, the silence in the streets, about how football not only imposes itself inside the stadiums but outside them too, in the roads, in the absence of people, in the vacuum. I kept my counsel and went to get my food, not wanting to ruin the opportunity for some good conversation by going off on a rant about "that sport". Or *futBOL*, as Naief was calling it, in his Mexican accent. Nevertheless, right in the middle of the buffet bar, I had to own up: I can't stand "that sport", I can't stand it to the point of not even being able to sit through a game, never mind stand the commentators and the journalists who cover it (though that's another matter).

Thankfully, my two colleagues were generous and seemed not to hold it against me. Miguel Ángel told us that he used to play when he was a boy, but that he gave it up once literature and computer games took over. Naief admitted he actually quite fancied watching the game and said he was going to take his food up to his room to do so. But then my favourite subject cropped up: lucha libre. I think maybe it was me who mentioned it when we were in the queue for the self-service or when we were just about to sit down, and this delayed his departure.

"It's the best sport in the world," I said. "It's a thousand times better than football."

The two sports, head to head: lucha libre versus football.

I launched into a long (and I imagine rather tedious) speech on the popularity of El Santo in Bolivia and how not so long ago I'd been lucky enough to see his grandson (Axel) fight in the great Coliseo Cerrado in La Paz. I shamelessly recounted how my legs had trembled when, while in the never-ending queue to get in, the woman standing next to me showed me the mask El Santo had given to her father, when El Santo had fought in La Paz in the Sixties.

As we ate, we spoke only of lucha libre. Naief recalled the *cholitas* and I said they were amazing wrestlers; Miguel Ángel stopped eating his pizza and asked what we meant by the term *chola*. He was from Central America and thought, or rather assumed, the word had something to do with *los cholos*, *los mareros*, those gang members covered in tattoos you'd do well to avoid. I explained that we were talking about Quechuan and Aymaran women in bowler hats, and I felt satisfied because it seemed lucha libre was holding off the threat of football, doing a *huracarana* on it, finishing it off with a *deacaballo* and a *martinete*. I went on: I told Naief and Miguel Ángel that the best wrestler around today was, in my opinion, El Místico, that he was the best wrestler I'd seen for several years and that the hold he'd invented was as beautiful and perfect as a short story by Edgardo Rivera. We took a pause, or rather the conversation went off in another direction: we talked of Facebook and Twitter and blogs and other things I still haven't managed to get my head round, and even then I felt satisfied: I'd frightened away the terrible football ghost that had been threatening to haunt our Quito night. But then someone (I don't remember who) asked about the match. Maybe it was the girl who'd been serving us who came over to the table and told us La Liga were now winning. They'd turned the game around and were now 2-1 up, or 3-1 up. The following scene sprang to mind: it's earlier in the day and I'm on the bus to the book fair and, oh look, what a coincidence, the Fluminense team are staying at the same hotel as us. My face is glued to the window as I stare at the back of the Brazilian bus: energy drinks, balls in string bags and there, piled on top, are three or four canisters of air. Quito is, unless I'm very much mistaken, 2,800 metres above sea level. The Fluminense squad had been complaining about this. As had my colleagues, their tongues hanging out as we made our way to the book fair, and an Argentinian lady fainted on the bus as it took us to dinner, and I laughed: these *gauchos* can't stomach anything. But revenge will be sweet: whenever I set foot back on Bolivian soil after being away I'm useless for several days, pale and weak. And I think: "It really is inhumane to play at this altitude."

We finished eating and walked over to the hotel, and still we hadn't talked about the passion of the masses (though in the short journey to the hotel door, the non-presence of football was even stronger). There was a television on in the hotel bar with a crowd of people (*quiteños* and outsiders) gathered around it, and at the precise moment we walked in they all screamed in celebration: La Liga had scored another goal. I'd lost, I thought, as I watched a bellboy run into the bar, smiling from ear to ear because his team was winning and, it seemed, close to becoming champions. But it was a defeat that tasted of victory, for football still hadn't won me over. The three of us stood there for a few moments, watching the pandemonium on screen as the footballers hugged, pumped fists and raised arms to the skies. We said our farewells and I made my tired way up to my room. Then the TV applied the final, fatal blow (in fact it had been applying it ever since my arrival): it was stuck on the same channel, or at least I couldn't figure out how to change the channel as I couldn't work the remote, and it was stuck on Fox Sports. I switched on just in time to see La Liga score another goal. I heard fireworks outside, indeed I could see them out of the window, and I knew it was going to be a long night: the party had only just begun; football had won. There was no chance lucha libre could stage a comeback. All night long, as I tried to sleep, I heard car horns in the streets; football's non-presence was no more, football was now manifest. La Liga were making history, or double history, as a bookseller explained to me at the fair the next day. I told him I hadn't seen the whole game, but that I'd been unable to sleep because of the racket. He asked me where I was from. I said Bolivia, and he talked of the altitude and said it was a shame we weren't going to the World Cup.

"Same as us," he said. "Though La Liga winning more than makes up for it."

Then he asked me who I thought would win the World Cup.

"I honestly don't even know who's playing in it."

With typical *quiteño* friendliness, the man listed all the teams going to South Africa. I heard him say Japan. And I thought of the manga cartoon *Captain Tsubasa*. The chance to make a comeback, I thought.

"In that case, Japan will probably win," I told him. "They've got some very good players."

"Really? Like who?" he asked.

"Oliver Tsubasa, Benji Wakabayashi, the Korioto brothers. With players like that, they'll win it for sure."

I paid for the book, he gave me my receipt and I left, satisfied that I'd finally got one over on football. But then doubt invaded me, doubts that have plagued me all my life. Did lucha libre really win? Did football win? Does it actually matter?

At the end of the week I found out La Liga had been crowned champions. I was pleased for them and for Quito, which deserves it for being so generous and so beautiful, and because of the great books I bought there. And I'm happy because of the Brazilians. It's good that they lost. I do a quick historical inventory and realise that there's never been a single Brazilian lucha libre wrestler of any merit. At least we're better than them at that, I think. And there's no chance of them staging a comeback. Although a few seconds later I'm not so sure and I scratch my head: or is there?

After living for ten years in New York, **Hernán Iglesias Illa** recently moved back to Buenos Aires, the city he was born and bred in. He is the author of three books, *Golden Boys* (2007), *Miami* (2010) and *American Sarmiento* (2013), and he has a webpage hernanii.net. In a normal week, he watches between eight and ten football matches on television.

'San Martín de Brooklyn Eye the Play-Offs' ('*San Martín de Brooklyn busca el repechaje*') was first published in *Orsai* magazine in January 2011.

SAN MARTÍN
DE BROOKLYN EYE
THE PLAY-OFFS

Hernán Iglesias Illa

Translated by Montague Kobbé

It was the first half of the second game of the season. We were play-ing a team of friendly and polite Ecuadorians, against whom we felt a *moral* obligation to win, and the score remained goalless. The referee awarded a corner in our favour. I'm a pretty lousy header of the ball, but I decided to put myself in the mix, throw myself into the horde of teammates and opponents, on the off chance of a miraculous rebound or miskick. I took part in the traditional mini stampede – ta-dum, ta-dum, ta-da-dum! – and watched the ball fly high, well over our heads, and then, with the attack seemingly over, I felt a push in my back, strong enough for me to feel I had the right to be angered. I identified the aggressor (an adolescent little sprat, slightly overweight, the look of an apprentice gang member) and we squared up to each other, chest to chest, both of us looking pretty ridiculous, awaiting who knows what. After a clumsy but brief tussle – I might have wielded a threatening fist at some point – I jogged solemnly back to the other end of the pitch, feeling proud of myself for having reacted so well to the provocation.

Hence my surprise when I saw the linesman waving his little flag as if a murder had taken place, and then the referee running towards him with the ominous urgency borne by referees running towards linesmen. They whispered to each other for the regulation ten seconds, the linesman's flag pointed in my direction and, a few seconds later, a red card popped out against the crystal clear Brooklyn sky, ruining a beautiful spring morning for me. Humiliated and ashamed, I walked slowly around the McCarren Park pitch, shin pads in hand, sky-blue top hanging over my shorts, thinking of how I would apologise to my teammates, the half-dozen Argentines, four or five *gringos*, two Paraguayans, a Colombian, a Uruguayan and an Italian, who come together on summer Saturdays to play for San Martín de Brooklyn in the Greenpoint Soccer League. A few locals from Williamsburg or Greenpoint jogged round the all-weather orange track at the pitch side; further away, others watched the match while they sunbathed, collected their dog's excrement or unfolded small tablecloths for imminent picnics.

The scene was extraordinary (twenty-two degrees, public facilities in good shape: the picture-postcard image of a happy neighbourhood), but I couldn't enjoy it: I'd promised my teammates that this season I'd avoid getting into trouble with referees, and I'd already failed. Besides, we'd agreed to give it everything this year to try and qualify for the league play-offs for the first time, after two pretty bad years (thirteenth out of sixteen teams in 2008; fourteenth out of twenty in 2009). And to achieve this we needed to win games like the one against the kindly Ecuadorians, El Progreso FC, a bunch of uncles, nephews and in-laws who'd all emigrated to the United States from the same suburb of Ambato in the Ecuadorian sierra and who'd finished the previous year in eighteenth place.

A couple of months earlier, in the windowless dining room of the Peruvian restaurant, Pío Pío, in Greenpoint, twenty team captains and a couple of curious tag-alongs had gathered for the annual captains' meeting of the Greenpoint Soccer League. Eating chicken with rice and fried plantain, courtesy of the league, some captains complained about the quality of refereeing, others demanded compensation when matches were cancelled ("Who pays my players' taxi fares?" complained the captain of a team that sometimes hires semi-professional players), while others asked for more rigorous measures to be taken against teams whose fans get drunk and insult or spit at opponents. (The previous year, the fans of Real Hidalgo, standing right on the touchline, had targeted me throughout the entire game: "Give it up, granddad!" one of them kept yelling at me. "Make way for the young generation!")

Meanwhile, I requested a technological revolution. At some point during the evening, I raised my hand and asked Gildardo Revilla, lord and master of the league, if we couldn't perhaps create a humble website to publish the results, fixtures and league tables. Revilla, who likes me and is fed up of me in almost equal measure, lowered his eyes, somewhat fatigued by my insistence, and offered a vague promise to think about it. The other captains were less receptive: as I spoke, I heard tutting, laughter breaking out in the shadows, as if the Internet was a thing for women or *gringos*, and had nothing to do with football.

Revilla, a short and astute Peruvian who has managed the league for almost twenty years, gave us notice of a few changes for the coming season (an increase in referee fees, "zero tolerance" for fan violence) and reminded us all of the tournament rules: twenty teams in a round-robin league, the top twelve qualifying for the play-offs, then eight going on to the quarter-finals, then semi-finals and the final. The winner of the regular season takes home US$1,500 in cash; the winner of the play-offs another US$2,000. We all nodded, as if we all truly believed we could win it (the contenders are always the same four or five teams), and one by one we waited our turn to hand Revilla's wife/assistant a fistful of notes as a deposit to seal our registration. I saw my fellow captains approaching Revilla's cubicle – almost all of them Latino, almost all of them immigrants, almost all of them working class – and once again felt the distance that has opened up over the years between myself and Revilla, my team and the rest of the league.

On the one hand, I feel, we feel, close to them, because we share the Latino condition and the football bug, two things the rest of New York doesn't have, doesn't understand and can't learn; but on the other hand, I feel, we feel, inevitably somewhat removed, because we know that in other aspects of our lives we represent the *gringo* New York they view from a distance and with distrust. Over the course of the three years we've taken part in the tournament, this tension – middle class versus working class, legal immigrant versus illegal immigrant, fluent English versus stuttering English, eating in restaurants versus *working* in restaurants – has ebbed and flowed, but it has always been there: at times, some of us have thought that Revilla or the referees have acted against us because we were not part of the "hard core" of Peruvian, Ecuadorian and Mexican teams in the league, and perhaps because they thought, somewhat justifiably, that we were part of the middle-class vanguard that had, for the past decade, been encroaching on Brooklyn from Manhattan, turning working-class neighbourhoods into hip ones, full of Japanese restaurants and interior-design shops, destroying and displacing everything it finds in its way.

San Martín de Brooklyn started the season in typically lacklustre fashion: a defeat by the narrowest of margins against a better team, a laboured victory against El Progreso FC (following my dismissal, my teammates won 3-1), an abominable 0-0 draw against a gang of battling but unskilled Uruguayans and a 2-1 reversal that looks respectable on paper but was actually a humiliating footballing lesson.

The fifth game got us up and running. In the third minute of his first game in our starting XI, Claudio, a feisty, quick and free-scoring Paraguayan, who had joined us after playing against us a few weeks earlier, broke free of his marker on the left wing, lost the ball, recovered it, lost it again, recovered it again, and drilled in a low cross that came to a stop in the D at the edge of the eighteen-yard box. I, who had been accompanying him more as a bystander than as a potential outlet for a pass, found the ball at the fringes of my left boot and hit it almost full, trying to bend it so that it would curve out at first and then come back inside the near post; the ball flew far higher than I intended, but it caught a lot more spin, eluded the keeper's outstretched hand and crept inside the far post. (I celebrated with great moderation, as if I were used to scoring such wonder goals.) They equalised towards the end of the first half, with a penalty that should never have been given, and then we scored again from the edge of the eighteen-yard box, in the very last minute. Just after our goal, while my teammates were celebrating, I shouted, "Despite the referee!" and was shown my one and only yellow card for dissent all season.

The following week we scored an equaliser at the death of a match we deserved to lose, but then our positive mini-streak came to an end, and we began our usual, almost inevitable, slide into the swamp we ended up in every summer. We won only two games between the middle of June and the end of August (against teams that would finish fourteenth and twentieth respectively) and lost every single other match, playing lousy football and barely scoring any goals. It's hard to play at McCarren Park when it's thirty-two or thirty-four degrees, as we had to do on a number of occasions, but our greatest problem that summer was a lack of players, because our North American teammates, and some of us Latinos too, had begun to prefer, due to family pressure or of our own volition, to spend Saturdays at the beach or on holiday. The Greenpoint Soccer

League is so not *gringo* that there are even games on public holidays, from Memorial Day in May to Labour Day in September. On July 4, 2009, Independence Day, we played at night, through the racket and under the filigree of New York's famous fireworks, while our American players (and the rest of the city) drank beer, ate sausages and rolled joints on their or someone else's terrace. The following year, the summer just gone, friends invited us to spend the weekend at a house in Connecticut, three hours away from New York. I suggested to my wife that she go with our friends on the Saturday morning, while I played against Los Hobos first and then took a train that would drop me in Connecticut at seven in the evening. My wife, who has learnt to pick her fights, agreed. When I arrived in McCarren Park that Saturday, there was no game under way. "You're going to have to excuse me, Hernán," Revilla said, opening his arms, "but there's been a misunderstanding between the captains of Real Hidalgo and Misfits and they haven't kicked off yet. Everything's behind schedule." I insulted Revilla like I'd not insulted anyone for a long time, and headed for the train station, my little bag slung over my shoulder, furious at having got the worst of both worlds: deprived of my working-class football and my bourgeois holiday.

On August 14, with the bulk of our first XI back from their travels, and following a series of results that left us a long way off but still with a *mathematical* chance of making the play-offs, we played against a team called New York United, which at the time lay in seventh place. To rally ourselves in the week leading up to the game, we exchanged emails full of football clichés: "Saturday's a must-win game", "From now on, our every game's a cup final", "The whole season hinges on this game!"

A couple of months later, I went to McCarren Park to watch the second legs of the quarter-finals. It was a chilly early-October night and the pitch looked beautiful, lit up like a stage inside the touchlines, dark and shadowy beyond, hundreds of people standing watching, hands in pockets, gently bouncing up and down to shake off the surprising early-autumn cold. On the pitch, two of the few multi-national teams in the league faced each other. Dream Team, wearing an old Inter Milan away kit, combined an ageing Ecuadorian core with reinforcements (or indeed replacements) from all over the world: two of their best players were an elegant, skinny Hungarian, whom they called "Eli", and an African-American centre-forward who went by the name of "Winsy"; Winsy had already scored over thirty goals. The other team was New York United, which featured a handful of Latinos, though not enough to tip the language barrier: they called for the ball ("Switch!" "Drop!"), encouraged each other ("Good ball") and gave orders ("Back, back!" "Pressure!") in English.

I soon found Revilla, standing near the halfway line, his little white cap pressed down to his ears, talking to the linesman. As soon as he saw me, he came over with a smile on his lips: "I was going to write you a letter, to explain some of the things you said about me on the Internet." I knew full well what he was talking about: in June and July, during the World Cup in South Africa, I'd written an online diary, and I'd devoted a handful of paragraphs to talking about him. I'd not been aggressive towards him, but I had been moderately sarcastic, especially about his overly elaborate system for deciding kick-off times, which leaves no room for negotiation or exception. Those who complain the most about the system are the middle-class teams, since because of it we can't "plan" our weekends and fit football into our (allegedly) varied menu of options. Until Tuesday night, when the captains call Revilla on his mobile, no team knows what time they'll be playing that Saturday (the first match is at eleven o'clock in the morning, the last at ten o'clock at night). Revilla is so in love with his system (he sets the times according to a mysterious ranking based on the two teams' positions in the league table) that he wouldn't even agree to make concessions so that the teams of Argentines, Uruguayans, *gringos* and Mexicans could watch their countries' World Cup games.

"You complain about the heat, about the times, about all the things we've discussed a thousand times," Revilla said to me that night. "But what you don't know is how difficult it is to organise all this, the number of complaints there are, the number of requests I have to deal with." I explained to Revilla that I understood perfectly well his predicament, and that I'd said precisely that in my column, but he didn't want to know. I realised he was playing with me, that he was more flattered than he was upset, and that he was aiming for a psychological victory. He placed his hands side by side and moved his fingers around, typing on an invisible keyboard, and he said, almost bursting out with laughter: "Did you think I wouldn't go on the Internet? Ha, ha, I found you out." I remained silent, smiling, somewhat excited to see that someone as old-fashioned as Revilla had also fallen prey to self-Googling, that he'd looked himself up, as we've all done, on the great web of webs. (The Greenpoint Soccer League is such an analogue tournament that it has barely left any trace on the Internet: it is *un-Googleable*. The search "Greenpoint Soccer League" produces half a dozen results, but none of them have anything to do with the league.)

After the game, a friend of Revilla's came over and we started talking about how you can tell where a player is from just by the way he walks on the pitch. "Argentinians, Uruguayans, Peruvians, you see them standing on the pitch, and even before they've kicked a ball, you know they're footballers," Revilla said. And *gringos*? Revilla sighed heavily, for he doesn't like to speak ill of the country in which he is also a citizen, but he admitted: "No, no, not the whities. Not the whities." *The whities.* An hour earlier I had asked Revilla where the New York United players were from and he'd said something similar: "I don't know. I think they're whities." But United's players, who wore Real Sociedad shirts and did, on *average*, have lighter skin than most Ecuadorian or Mexican teams, came from countries that could hardly be qualified as "whitey": there were Puerto Ricans, Romanians, Chileans, even a couple of Ecuadorians. "Mexicans are clumsy," Revilla then said. "But they dig deep. You score one, two goals, and you have to make it three-nil or four-nil to beat them, because if you're only two goals up, they'll throw everything at you and end up equalising." What about Peruvians? "We Peruvians are skilful," Revilla said, with a combination of pride and resignation. "The problem is we lack discipline."

His description of Peruvian players pretty much tallied with what we'd noticed on the pitch ourselves: like Peru's national side, Peruvian teams tended to be talented but harmless; they could pass the ball around nicely, but would inexplicably go to pieces at the first setback. But his description of Mexican teams didn't correspond with our experience: we didn't find them clumsy at all, though they were also pretty similar to their national side: quick but unreliable defenders, slow but majestic centre-midfielders, and a couple of tireless wingers who constantly ran at you, in diagonal lines like bishops, and were capable of creating danger at any moment.

A common sight at McCarren Park is for the only tall players on a Mexican or Ecuadorian team – comprised, for the most part, of short and sometimes rather overweight players – to be a couple of *gringos*, Jamaican or Senegalese players standing at centre-half and centre-forward. These guys – some of whom are on summer holidays from university scholarships, others who are seasoned urban footballers from parks in Randall Island or Flushing Meadows – get paid between US$40 and US$80 per game, and play four or five games per weekend in leagues spread around the entire city. Since their Spanish-speaking teammates don't know them very well and don't know their names, they call for the ball by loudly screaming "*Negro, negro!*" which in this quasi-playground hardly even registers on the barometer of political incorrectness. In the years we've been playing in the Greenpoint Soccer League, one of the best strikers has always been a sharp, nifty little player, whose name has never been learnt by his Mexican teammates: "Arab, Arab!" they call to him, and the little guy, the spitting image of Diego Buonanotte, just turns and smiles.

The game against New York United, the most important game of our lives, lasted about half an hour. After that, it ceased being a contest and turned into an exhibition (by them) and an exercise in torture (for us). They scored their first goal in the twelfth or thirteenth minute, their second in the twenty-fifth or twenty-sixth, their third just before half-time. We'd started the game feeling euphoric, although we were in a bit of a daze even before they landed their first punch, after which we slowly fell, as if being blown to the deck. We ended the game feeling grumpy, silently making our way back to the small tree where our wives awaited us, ready to ask, with the best of intentions but no tact: "Did you win?" Some of us let out sardonic, almost evil cackles, testament to the shame and indignation we felt at losing 5-0 in the one game we had to win at all costs.

The following Tuesday we analysed the handwritten, photocop-ied sheet of the league tables and called Revilla to ask him about the results of the other games – sometimes he remembers, sometimes he's not so sure ("I think Guadalupe won...") – and did the maths: our only option for finishing in the top twelve was to win our four remaining games.

On the evening of August 21, we played against Universidad Católica, a team of Peruvians and Mexicans sitting sixth in the table. We were fourteenth and had never beaten a team placed above us. I scored in the first half to put us 1-0 up, tapping in at the near post from a brilliant cross whipped in by John, one of our *gringos*, and Claudio gave us a two-goal cushion sometime later, finishing with his left foot after latching on to my through-ball, one of those passes I used to serve up by the dozen a few years ago, but which with age and diminished confidence had become few and far between.

The following Saturday we played Real Hidalgo, the previous year's champions. We pretended we were doomed, like characters in a Greek tragedy, and the trick worked: they believed us and, more importantly, so did we, allowing us to play free of pressure, brimming with confidence, hardly able to believe our own resilience and energy, until Pietro, our Italian forward, scored a penalty and then fired over a cross that Claudio headed in at the far post. We pinched each other at half-time, as if wanting to waken from a dream. They tried to steamroller through us in the second half, and they nearly managed it: they made it 2-1 and for a moment it seemed like San Martín would go back to being its usual shaky, hesitant self. But with two minutes to go, Matías, who had spent the whole season chasing opponents around the middle of the pitch, hit a right-footed rocket into the top corner and screamed so loud the whole park turned round to look at him. We won the next game by default (Honduras FC having withdrawn from the tournament) and won our final game 4-0, as if goalscoring had always come easy to us. At the end of the game we looked at each other and could hardly believe it: despite sabotaging our own campaign for weeks on end, we'd finished the tournament in eleventh place, earning twenty-nine points from nineteen games, and the right to flirt, at least for a little while, with the footballing aristocracy of the Greenpoint Soccer League.

Until relatively recently, several teams used Saturdays not only as a sporting occasion but as a social event: they would hang out in the park, eating fruit and sandwiches, listening to music and drinking beer, till way past midnight. When they needed to go for a slash, they did so against the walls of the abandoned factories. Now that those factories had been replaced by apartment buildings, Revilla was obliged to ask them to please stop "urinating" near the buildings. "Where should we go instead?" some protested at the captains' meeting in Pío Pío. "Do it at the other end of the park, against the baseball stands," the president of the league suggested.

I paid Revilla a visit one Saturday and found him walking around the pitch with a cane in one hand and a bag in another, collecting up rubbish – empty bottles of Gatorade, plastic bags, food leftovers – left behind by the crowds who'd watched the games that day. I asked him how much the neighbourhood had changed in the almost twenty years he'd been organising the tournament. Revilla stopped, turned around and looked at the apartment buildings that had been built during the property boom that burst in 2008. "This was all factories," he said, raising both arms and pointing east and south. "All factories. There wasn't a single residential building."

McCarren Park, the municipal park where the tournament takes place, is located on the eastern end of Williamsburg, a neighbourhood that over the past decade and a half has gone from being a semi-dodgy, semi-Polish, semi-empty city outpost, to becoming a refuge for artists and rockers, and – in a second transition, connected to the first – a cool and expensive neighbourhood with "alternative" boutiques and Scandinavian-style furniture shops. What happened in Williamsburg had happened countless times before, across the entire city: as yuppies and other youngsters get tired of the suburbs and move back into city centres, they displace the bohemian, lumpen creatives who lived almost rent-free in derelict neighbourhoods such as SoHo or the East Village. The bohemian, lumpen creatives (artists, musicians, designers) took refuge in Brooklyn, on the other side of the East River, where they opened art galleries and little restaurants that slowly displaced the black or Dominican families that had been living there for the previous thirty years. The tendency – dubbed "gentrification" by some, even in Spanish: *gentrificación*, a bluntly phonetic translation of the English term – has slowed down but remains a constant, reaching into regions that are further and further away from Brooklyn and Upper Manhattan.

For Revilla, who lives in the vicinity of the park but in the opposite direction, one still safe from yoga studios and organic-coffee emporiums, the main upside to Williamsburg's gentrification process is the transformation of McCarren Park: up until 2005 the Greenpoint Soccer League was played on a treacherous wasteland of weeds and rubble; since 2006 it has been played on an amazing floodlit pitch with state-of-the-art artificial turf. To some of the Latin Americans who play in the league, the park is among the most impressive benefits afforded them by the *gringo* state, a state that will not allow them the right to work, but will afford them the right to play football on a pitch that would be out of reach to them back home.

Revilla and numerous other Peruvians began playing in McCarren Park in the early 1990s, when it was surrounded by factories, cracked warehouses and the odd Polish bar or butcher's that spilt over from neighbouring Greenpoint. One afternoon, an officer from the Department of Parks and Recreation came to warn them they couldn't use the field without a permit, and left them his business card. Revilla called him, attended meetings and seminars, and in 1992 founded the Greenpoint Soccer League, which in its first edition featured eight teams, almost all of them Peruvian. As the years went by, the league grew and went through a process of *de-Peruvianisaion*, mirroring the migratory tendencies of the city. Fifteen years ago, there were few Mexicans in New York and few Mexicans in Revilla's tournament; these days the proportion of Mexicans is significantly higher, in restaurant kitchens and construction sites, and on the football fields of Brooklyn. "Peruvian teams no longer dominate," Revilla told me. "They started getting old, there's been no generational relay."

We went on to talk about his own story. He told me, with some of the usual hang-ups immigrants have, that he'd been in the United

States for thirty years, that he first came on his own and was only later able to bring his wife. The most painful thing, he told me, was having to leave his son behind in Peru, to be taken care of by his sister and his sister-in-law. In an interview he gave to a journalist from the website Peru21.pe (who met him through me), Revilla revisited those early years in more detail: "I went to Lima recently and my sister gave me the letters I used to send to my son [he waves a series of yellowed postcards dated from 1979 onward]. It was an emotional moment. These things happen. We battled hard for three years, got our papers in order and were finally able to summon my son. But one of the hardest things about being here [he pauses] is that I was never able to see my father again. When I eventually made it back, he'd already passed away. This country gives you good things, but it also asks for things in return."

Reading statements like this, I rather regret my troubled relationship with Revilla, a man I've fought with much more than necessary. I still don't understand why he has to be so inflexible and arbitrary with the fixture list, or why he resists (by conviction or indifference; at this stage it's practically the same thing) the idea of creating a simple website where everyone can access the league tables, other teams' results and the kick-off times of upcoming games. All these years, our only mathematical connection to the rest of the tournament has been a scribbled, photocopied sheet of paper that Revilla hands out every Saturday before the games. It is a league table devised with technology that harks back to the 1970s, more of a relic than a useful device, but something that I have gradually had less and less desire to protest against and fight.

Our flirt with the Greenpoint Soccer League elite was short-lived and brutal. We lost 3-0, dominated and overrun from the first minute to the last, against Filco, my favourite team in the league, a multi-Latino bunch who play passing, attacking football and wear

Barcelona's fluorescent pink top. While they played their football, we seemed ashamed of interrupting them. It would take us five minutes to win the ball back and ten seconds to lose it again; the ball went up in the air and three fluorescent shirts jumped for it versus a single sky-blue one; when we tried to *slow* the game down, pause for a moment (plead for a truce!), they didn't even notice: they rolled us over. "At least we achieved our target for the season," one of us said afterwards, consoling no one.

The final was played a month later. Filco and their fluorescent ballet dancers were in it, having turned every qualifying game into a goalfest, as were Dream Team, the league's equivalent of Chelsea, the side with the greatest number of paid players. I once asked Dream Team's coach and manager, an Ecuadorian with a small moustache and short hair, where he got his players from and he told me he went around scouting all the leagues in the city: "We look for players every-where, and the ones we like the most, the best of the best, we draft in," he replied. I was therefore supporting Filco, because they had fewer paid players (and I feel it a moral duty to support the team with the greater amateur spirit), but also because they'd knocked us out of the competition, and losing to the eventual champions is always a neat way of saving face and boosting your footballing self-esteem.

There was a cup-final atmosphere in the air. Revilla had placed a garden table pitchside to display the trophies, coated (or disguised) in marble and gold. Some 2,000 people had come to watch the game, filling the touchlines, on the verge of spilling onto the pitch, forc-ing the linesmen to stand inside the field of play and prompting a moment of uproar and confusion every time there was a throw-in. Among the spectators were Latinos and their families (sitting in little beach chairs, drinking coffee from Dunkin' Donuts, sharing bags of food) but also a number of people more reflective of the neighbourhood (bearded indie-band guitarists, freelance bloggers in skin-tight T-shirts, pale girls in flowery dresses with tattoos on their shoulders), enticed there by the energy of the occasion. The teams were evenly matched and it was a pretty good game. Eli, Dream Team's Hungarian star, controlled the tempo from his midfield hub, but Filco always found ways to create danger. In the second half, with the match level at one apiece, Dream Team's manager brought on a black Panamanian, beer-bellied and big-buttocked. The crowd greeted him with jeers and jibes, but I'd seen him play before and I was pleased when he played the most perfectly weighted of through-balls for Winsy to latch onto and score his thirty-eighth or thirty-ninth (Revilla had lost count) goal of the campaign. Filco, older than their opponents but with more guile, poured forward, played the percentages and eventually scored an equaliser, in the last minute, after launching their hundredth ball into the box and seeing the previous ninety-nine get cleared.

Everyone in the crowd celebrated the goal like it was their own, because it meant the drama would continue with a penalty shoot-out. The referee, a tall and skinny Peruvian with zero sense of humour, tried to stop everyone from encroaching onto the pitch, but no one listened to him. By the time Filco's left-back started his run-up to take the first penalty, the crowd had crept up to the edge of the eighteen-yard box, totally enclosing the penalty box and the penalty takers, lending the finale an atmosphere that was both tense and calm, something between a religious ceremony and a possible lynching. Before every penalty kick the spectators went totally silent, like at the theatre, and with every goal they broke into tiny fits of joy or disappointment. When Dream Team's Mexican keeper, the best of the tournament, caught the only miscued penalty of the night, the Ahhhhs and Ohhhhs of the numerous *gringos* in the crowd were clearly heard, because they might not know much about football, but they know a good show when they see one.

While some partied, others rued their luck, and thousands more headed home, or to wherever it was they had to get to. Revilla called me to one side and asked me to act as translator in the awards ceremony. Filco's manager was first up, a man who is boss to most of his team on and off the pitch: the majority of Filco's players work under him at a waste-recycling company. He took home a tall golden trophy delightfully inscribed: "Sub-Champion 2010". Then the Dream Team's players approached. "You will receive your medals from Mr Hernán, here, from the San Martín team," said Revilla, and the champions lined up before me while I, feeling rather flattered but also rather uncomfortable, lifted the medals over their sweaty heads and let them drop round their necks. Revilla took a trophy from the table and said in Spanish: "*El premio al goleador!*" Then he looked at me: "Translate!" I stuttered: "The award for top scorer..." but it wasn't necessary: Winsy's teammates had already pushed him forward and he lifted the little trophy aloft, shy and happy. "*El mejor jugador!*" Revilla then said. "The best player..." I echoed, in a low voice. Revilla, who didn't know the guy's name, pointed a finger at Eli, and the Hungarian, whose looks and manners are of a different era, as if he's escaped from a black-and-white movie, wielded his trophy just as sheepishly. Revilla then turned round, was passed an envelope by his wife, and handed it over to the Ecuadorian with the small moustache: "Count it," he said. Dream Team's manager opened up the envelope and counted it: US$2,000 exactly.

Afterwards, when just the two of us were left, I congratulated Revilla on a successful final: good football, a good attendance and a dramatic conclusion. "Yes, it was good," he said, tired or melancholic. Then, so as to complete the patching-up of our relationship, I congratulated him on the league, telling him how much I admired his devotion, and emphasising that, while we might still disagree on some things, I considered playing in the Greenpoint Soccer League an enthralling experience, the highlight of my summer. Revilla thanked me, but then he pointed in the direction of the apartment blocks around us, where amber-coloured windows spoke of the warmth of middle-class homes. "This league has three or four years left, five at the most," he told me. Somewhat taken aback, I asked him what made him think that. "It's obvious, brother. They'll push us out. This pitch is too pretty for us to carry on using. At some point they'll take it away from us." I remained silent, thinking about whether Revilla had any reason to be so pessimistic. I didn't know the answer. I asked myself: if some kind of judgement were eventually made, what side would Revilla think we were on? It was a question I was reluctant to answer. "The whities are coming, Hernán," Revilla then said, perhaps answering for me. "The whities are coming."

TEJEDA

12

Agustín del Moral Tejeda. Las Choapas, Veracruz, Mexico, 1956. He has had the following works co-published by the Universidad Veracruzana Editorial and Ficticia publishing houses: *Cuéntame lo que me pasa* (2009, shorts), *Nuestra alma melancólica en conserva* (2nd edition, 2005, novel), *Un crack mexicano: Alberto Onofre* (2003 and 2005, creative non-fiction).

'The Mexican Pelé' is an extract taken from *Un crack mexicano: Alberto Onofre*.

THE MEXICAN PELÉ

Agustín del Moral Tejeda

Translated by Jethro Soutar

We were realistic. We knew that if we played to our potential we could go further than Mexico had ever gone at a World Cup before. But no, we didn't think we could win it. We had home advantage, and our preparations were excellent: we'd been gathered together at a training camp for five months, and had played several international friendlies (against the likes of Belgium, Denmark, England, Norway, Yugoslavia, Brazil...); we even played an away game in Peru, if I recall. Basically everything you could ask for. But no, not enough to make us think we could win the World Cup.

The training camp began in early January. We trained twice a day: once in the morning, once in the afternoon. We got up at seven and trained until nine, had breakfast and rested until two in the afternoon. Then we trained again, from two until four, washed, ate and had the rest of the day free. The players who were from Mexico City went off to see their families. The rest of us went out for a coffee, to the cinema, to see a friend. I remember I used to meet up with David Rodríguez, a mate who's been with me through thick and thin. We'd meet in the restaurant at El Emperador, the hotel Guadalajara used to use when we played in Mexico City. I'd meet David there, and we'd have a coffee and a chat. Sometimes one of the players who lived in Mexico City would invite me to his house, to meet his family or go on a trip somewhere. Other times I stayed at the training camp and watched telly, or read.

The important thing was to keep things varied, otherwise you'd go stir crazy. But whatever you did, you had to be back at the training camp by eight, when dinner was served. And then off to bed.

It was a very focused training camp. Those of us who lived outside Mexico City were only allowed to go and visit our families on a handful of occasions. Four or five times at most, over a period of five months, and even then only for a day or two, a weekend or something like that. Nevertheless, we really appreciated those trips. It's easy to imagine: cohabiting (eating, sleeping, exercising, training – basically doing everything) for five months, with the same people, in the same place, gets pretty tedious. No matter how much we were united by a common goal, five months is a long time. Besides, you have to remember that everyone's aim at the camp was to win a place in the team, and we were all prepared to do whatever it took to achieve that aim. Inevitably you get a bit of everything in a training camp like that: tensions, frictions, problems, disputes... We were only human, we had our egos, our jealousies, our rivalries... all related to getting into the team. So a few days off were like a breath of fresh air: you took yourself out of the pressure-cooker environment of the camp, you travelled, you went home, spent time with loved ones, who were very understanding of course. You came back rejuvenated.

Bit by bit, the team started to take shape. As ever, it was a slow and difficult process, starting from scratch. It's not easy to mould players together from different teams. Everyone has different styles of play, some of them totally opposite: some like to play open, attacking football, others prefer to keep things tight and defensive; some are used to one particular system, others to another. In those five months Güero Cárdenas tried everything, alternating players, positions and formations, until finally, slowly but surely, a team began to form and we really started to play as a unit. I'd say that by the end of May we'd peaked as a team.

To be totally honest, the whole game plan revolved around me. It's perhaps not my place to say that, but that's the way it was: I was the only definite in the starting line-up. I may be wrong, but I'm pretty sure I was the only player who played in all the warm-up games. Güero Cárdenas tried out different players in every position but mine. I was confirmed as the attacking midfielder. This all placed a heavy burden on me, but it was a burden I was ready to bear. For up until then I'd managed to achieve everything I'd set out to achieve: to become a first-team regular for the Chivas, to break into the national team, to play in the World Cup. My next objective was to play abroad. Back then it was unusual for Mexicans to play overseas. Many years would have to pass until Hugo Sánchez came along and established himself internationally. But even though it sounded – how shall I put it? – somewhat incredible or ambitious, my aim was to play abroad, to play internationally. Where? I don't know. All I know is that I wanted to play outside of Mexico. And the only way to achieve that aim was by having a good World Cup, by standing out, by being one of the best, if not the best. I knew I had the ability to do it. Therefore, although I did feel the burden of responsibility, I was ready for it, ready to lead Mexico's attack.

I think my leadership was generally well accepted within the squad. It was a given as far as the other Guadalajara players were concerned; I think they were even quite proud to see a Chivas teammate as the linchpin of the national team. As for players from other teams, I think they accepted me too... generally speaking. I remember there was a bit of jealousy from the more senior players, those who were quite renowned back then, big names, some of whom had even played at the World Cup before: Peña, Borja... I think they were a little aggrieved. It can't have been easy for them to accept such a young player as leader – I was only twenty-two years old.

My relationship with the press changed too. Or rather, the press changed the way they treated me. When my form dipped as a centre-forward for the Chivas, they gave me a pretty hard time... hunters moving in for the kill. But when I dropped into midfield and recovered my form, as I began to prove myself as a creative midfielder, as the

Chivas were crowned champions and I was named player of the season and called up to the national team... things changed. Suddenly it was non-stop praise and recognition. Curiously, looking back, I think I learnt a lot more from the criticism. Praise can be stimulating, but it makes it harder for you to see your faults. Criticism, on the other hand, even if it knocks the stuffing out of you, allows you to see where you're going wrong, what you need to work and improve on. In any case, I learnt not to shrink from the criticism, but to move on, let it build my character. Praise I treated as a bonus, trying not to get carried away.

There were three days to go until the start of the World Cup. We would train on Thursday, take Friday and Saturday as rest days and then play the opening game on the Sunday. Thursday was our last training session. The last training session! It was an overcast afternoon, rainy. The pitch was soft and wet. Training was coming to an end. Five more minutes and Güero Cárdenas would have blown his whistle. The last five minutes! I challenged for the ball with Juan Manuel Alejándrez, a holding midfielder from Cruz Azul. I slipped, lost my footing and went into the tackle with limp legs, or rather with my left leg skidding out of control and my right leg up in the air. My left ankle twisted, and I tumbled to the ground. Alejándrez, on the other hand, came into the tackle strong, his legs firm. The inevitable collision occurred. We hit each other hard. I was winded and even lost consciousness for a few seconds. When I came round, all I could feel was a sharp pain in my left leg. I knew straight away I was injured.

"Guadalajara Football Club," I said and got in. After a couple of minutes of jovial chit-chat from the taxi driver (he was a *chiva* too and delighted that an out-of-towner had come to visit "the home of a national sporting institution, for that's what the Chivas are, am I right, my good man?"), I picked up his newspaper and pretended to read. Pretended, for I couldn't concentrate: like a murderer returning to the scene of a crime, memories came flooding back:

unstoppable memories, bruising memories, bitter-sweet memories, as I travelled back in time, to my youth, to the hopes and dreams of a boy who wanted nothing more in life than to play centre-forward for Guadalajara. I recalled my skinny, slight frame, a training session for Veracruz juniors; I recalled Montes, the coach, desperately trying to make me understand my role and my position; I recalled the day I fucked it all up, storming off the pitch in a huff, ruining my fledgling football career...

"Here we are, my good man," the taxi driver interrupted my reveries. I folded up his newspaper, put it back on the dashboard and paid up. In a desperate attempt to make up for my unsociable, somewhat rude attitude, I let fly with a few words to put a smile back on his face: "Thank you – and up the Chivas, my good man!"

Only once the taxi driver had pulled away did I turn my attention to the training ground and the giant red, white and blue letters adorning the roof of the main building: Club Deportivo Guadalajara, AC.

I asked someone where the first team trained and was told to head over to the other side of the complex. I walked and walked, until my progress was finally blocked by a mesh fence. An inter-squad match was under way: first-teamers intent on cementing their status; reserves trying to force their way into the side. I immediately recognised names, numbers, positions, physiques, mannerisms: Claudio Suárez, Alberto Coyote, Benjamín Galindo, Ramón Ramírez, Luis García, Ricardo Peláez, Tuca Ferretti, the coach, and... Who was that standing next to Tuca?... His outline, his thin body, his eagle-like nose, his lank hair – though visibly greying – was all somehow familiar... I went back to watching the game. I listened to Tuca shouting instructions and recriminations: several times he stopped the game in order to get his point across more forcefully, or brought play back to go over something again, to fine-tune details. I listened to him as he constantly discussed things with... who? Who was the guy standing next to him? He looked so familiar, but my memory refused to cooperate. Then he stood up, came over to the touchline, shouted at Ramón, made signals for him to play further up the field, and went back to the dugout. Was that a limp? Did he have a slight limp, or was I imagining it? It was hard to tell at such a distance. But was it?... Could it be?...

I moved around, seeking a better angle (no easy thing with so many other fans there watching) and tried to focus on team formation, work out the tactics, the interplay – the source of the free-flowing style the team was known for at the time... But over and over again, my gaze kept returning to – what should I call him? – to this "character", whom I was sure I'd seen before, perhaps many years ago...

I got caught up in all the crying out, the clapping and the banter, and started to join in myself, hailing a clearance by Claudio, a great tackle by Coyote, a lovely feint by Ramón, a quick-fire shot by Luis... And then the "character" himself came onto the pitch and stopped the game, and yes, he did have a slight limp, and he summoned Galindo over and called for the ball, placed it just beyond the centre circle, rearranged the defence, pushed the ball forward, ran with it, skipped past a man, then another, and then – what poise, what skill, what class! – put a through-ball in to Peláez, finding the gap, threading it right into the danger zone... Oh yes, now I was almost certain it was him...

I waited for the training session to end. The players filed off the field slowly, in dribs and drabs, boots slung over shoulders, bodies shaking, sweating, visibly exhausted. The supporters swarmed round them, hunting for autographs, waving pieces of paper, photographs, a shirt, a ball. I stood there for a moment, proud and dignified, charmed by the scene, by everyone's sense of attachment and devotion to the Chivas colours. I stood there for a moment, curious and entertained, listening to the tributes, to men turned into heroes by the shirts on their backs: "You played a blinder!..." "We've got the league sewn up this year..." "You're a genius, Luis..." I stood there and for a moment

I almost lunged forward to ask Galindo for his autograph, a fib at the tip of my tongue – "Thanks, Benjamín, it's for my daughter."

But I wasn't waiting for the players. I was waiting for the mysterious figure, the surprise of the afternoon, the "character". And there he was, walking slowly, chatting away to Tuca and Coyote. My suspicions were confirmed the closer he got. Yes, it was obvious now. His face, his skin, his hair, his walk; all bore testimony to the passage of time, but there was no doubt about it, it was him: Alberto Onofre.

As soon as Tuca, Coyote and Onofre stepped off the training pitch, the autograph hunters launched themselves at the first two. Unperturbed, Onofre stepped to one side and leant back against the mesh fence. There he remained, perhaps waiting for Tuca and Coyote to free themselves up to carry on their conversation, perhaps enjoying the spectacle, perhaps recalling old times, or all these things rolled into one. Shielded by the fans crowded around Luis García, I moved discreetly and positioned myself fifteen feet away from Onofre, the better to observe him, to compare my distant memories to the flesh-and-bone man I saw before me, to confirm that it really was him.

Then I made up my mind. Swerving round the autograph hunters and remaining players, I placed myself before him. By now I had no doubt who he was, but I went through the formalities anyway. "You're Alberto Onofre, aren't you?" I asked him. "At your service, sir," he replied with a smile. I introduced myself. I kept it brief. I told him I was a *chiva*, that I'd come all the way from Veracruz and that I'd very much like to talk to him, maybe invite him for lunch at the club restaurant. "It would be my pleasure, sir," he said. "Just let me finish up with Tuca." He headed over to the huddle with the coach at its centre and politely got Tuca's attention, making signals at first, then calling out his name. Tuca excused himself and went over to Onofre. They resumed their conversation and carried it on for several minutes.

"All yours, sir," I heard at my side. I followed him over to the restaurant, stopping off at the souvenir shop on the way. I bought a navy-blue blanket for my wife, the red-and-white striped shirt for my daughter and a history of Guadalajara Football Club for myself. Naturally I got Onofre to sign all three. We got to the restaurant and ordered: a simple sandwich and a coke for him; for me, the *birria* stew and... my first tequila. Conversation flowed, topics bursting forth in quick succession: the Chivas, the club's history, the current team, bygone eras, great players, greatest achievements. After covering the history of the club, we moved on to his own story. Did people still remember? Naturally, not so many any more, and those that did, only vaguely: something that rang a bell, sounded familiar. I remembered it perfectly, I always would. It was the story of the finest Mexican centre-midfielder I ever saw: cerebral, skilful, precise, purposeful, blessed with extraordinary vision, two-footed, a good header of the ball, charismatic, loved and respected by teammates, a true leader, the sort of player who stations himself in the middle of the park and dictates the course of play – the one-in-a-million player who comes along so rarely, pulling the strings for the Chivas and the national team. Raúl "El Güero" Cárdenas built the whole team around him for the 1970 World Cup. Everything was set for Mexico to be the surprise package, and for Onofre to show the rest of the world what we already knew: that he was a player of true international stature. Then days before the great carnival commenced, in a tragic accident at an ill-fated last training session, Alejándrez, a holding midfielder from Cruz Azul, injured him. Broke his left leg. That was that. He was out of the World Cup. He was hospitalised for several months, subjected to a series of surgeries. (I'll never forget a photo of him that appeared in *Futbol*, his left leg visibly crooked, a scar running from one end of his tibia to the other.) He tried to make a comeback. Somewhat oddly, perhaps to reduce the pressure, he was farmed out to the Chivas feeder club in Tijuana. In some edition of *Esto* I read about a great game, a complete all-round performance, the great field marshal reborn, the imminent return of the crack player. But it never happened. He never recovered (and nor, it's said, did Alejándrez).

I told him what he'd meant to me in my adolescence, all those years when I dreamt of becoming a professional footballer, when he was my idol, my role model, a paradigm at a time when I desperately needed someone to emulate. I explained what a terrible shock his injury had been to me. I remembered the moment perfectly: it was the weekend and I'd just got home from football training. I went straight into the kitchen to get a drink, still wearing my kit and my boots. My sister had the telly on in the lounge and was watching the quarter-to-eight evening news on Canal 2. When I heard the voice of Fernando Marcos, the sports presenter, I rushed in. It was the very first news item. The look on Marcos's face was one of utter despair, dejection and defeat: an expression that conveyed the sense of tragedy even before his words could. He spoke, fully aware of what the news meant to us all: to Onofre, to the Mexican team, to the millions of people preparing to cheer Mexico on at the World Cup. Of all that he said, only two things lodged in my brain: Onofre was injured; Onofre was out of the World Cup. That was enough. I went up to my room and shut the door. I threw myself on the bed and cried. It was perhaps the first time I'd shed tears for someone else. Of course, I was crying for myself, too, because my hero had fallen, was injured, was out of the running. But more than that, I was crying for Onofre, for his pain and tragedy and misfortune, for the injustice of it all. I didn't leave my room until the following day.

From his story we moved on to mine. By now, however, the unexpected encounter (with my team and my former hero), the memories (some pleasurable, some painful, some pleasurable but painful, some painful but pleasurable) and, above all, the tequilas, had transformed me. Circumstances got the better of me and took hold of my tongue. I became unrecognisable: vivacious, loquacious, effusive. And in this unfortunate condition, I began to talk about myself, to tell my story (if it can even be called a story), to speak of my hopes, my dreams, my failures. So far, so good (in a manner of speaking), until at a particular moment I lost control, I ran riot, my tongue got the better of me: I established an unfortunate parallel between his story and mine; I even spoke of frustration as being our common denominator. That's as far as the conversation went. Up until then Onofre had been demure, discreet, reticent; now he cut me off:

"One moment, sir. I played for Guadalajara; I know what it's like to pull on the national team shirt. I made it. Afterwards, sure, I had my downfall, though through no fault of my own. And I picked myself up. It took hard work, but I managed it. I didn't make it back as a player, I accept that, but I got back into football. I advise the players, I assist the coach, I'm in charge of basic fitness, doing what I love, what comes naturally to me. I'm not, as you claimed a moment ago, full of pain and bitterness. If you want to call my story tragic, fine, that's up to you, but your story, forgive me, sir, but the way you tell it, yours is more pathetic than tragic. So our stories are not the same, frustration is not our common denominator. Occupational hazard... That's all it was. Now if you'll excuse me, I really have to get going."

I fell to pieces. Drunkenness drained out of me. Words deserted me. I couldn't even manage an apology. I simply followed him with my eyes, watched him pay his bill and disappear from sight, heading back out to the training pitches. Fortunately for me, nobody had heard our conversation. I decided to remain where I was, sitting at the table, to try to recover, catch my breath, clear my head. I raised my hand and ordered a coffee. I flicked through the book, admired the photos, distracted myself with some caption or other, some snapshot from the club's history. I tried to read, to really read. But it was useless. I couldn't focus, couldn't let myself be distracted, couldn't escape.

José Pérez Reyes. Asunción, Paraguay, 1972. Writer, lawyer, university professor. He has had three collections of short stories published: *Ladrillos del tiempo* (2002), *Clonsonante* (2007; his best-known work) and *Asunscenarios* (2012). In 2007 he was named among the Bogotá39, a Hay Festival initiative recognising the continent's best young authors. His stories have been included in international anthologies in Colombia, Mexico, Cuba, Argentina, Chile, Portugal and Spain. He has had work translated into English and published by Words Without Borders in 2011. His webpage and blog can be found at joseperezreyes.blogspot.com. His work frequently combines Guaraní with Spanish: in 'Loyalty Card', the Guaraní words appear in italics.

'Loyalty Card' ('*Carnet de fiel consumidor*') was first published in *Asuncenarios* (Editorial Arandurá).

LOYALTY CARD

José Pérez Reyes

Translated by Tim Girven

STEWARD 1: Where's your loyalty card?

CITIZEN: Where's my what?

STEWARD 1: You have to show your consumer loyalty card to gain entry into the new stadium, everyone knows that.

STEWARD 2: It's the only document that counts. The basic hallmark of a good citizen.

CITIZEN: So, consume first, choose second, then vote – though it matters little who for, so long as I purchase?

STEWARD 2: Actually, what really matters is the frequency with which you shop, the fact that you're buying.

STEWARD 1: How often do you shop?

CITIZEN: This seems more like an interrogation than an ID check to enter the ground.

STEWARD 1: As everyone knows: "Citizenship is a thing of the past; store-card use determines your class."

STEWARD 2: "Purchasing power is all that matters."*

CITIZEN: What on earth are you talking about?

STEWARD 1: Didn't you take your induction? The number on your card and, above all, the consumption levels registered on the card... That's your key document. You have to consume constantly to stay up to date. Jesus, this guy doesn't know *guaú*.

---

* Both phrases come from the official manual *Aqui$itive MotiVATion*.

CITIZEN: This is bullshit! Total *vyreza*. You should be grateful there are still people who come to the ground to watch the game, instead of slobbing on the sofa at home in front of the telly. The only thing I have on me is my NIC.

STEWARD 1: NIC? What's that stand for? Nominal Investor Credits?

CITIZEN: National Identity Card!

STEWARD 1: Oh, they're no longer valid. I thought you were talking about some new pay-as-you-go membership scheme.

CITIZEN: *Mba'échaguá oficiales!* What kind of officials are you? How can you not recognise national documentation?

STEWARD 1: Look, just show us your loyalty card or hop it. That's all we accept these days, Gramps, OK?

CITIZEN: I'm going to lodge a formal complaint. I'm going to put it up online right now.

STEWARD 1: Listen, old boy, if I sound this alarm here, you'll soon see...

STEWARD 2: Oh, let him be, *when he wer' a lad, the net were the goal, not the web*. If he's not a registered consumer, he obviously won't have any followers.

CITIZEN: Online or in the newspaper, whatever: I'm going to write a complaint!

STEWARD 2: Newspaper? What the... No one reads the papers any more.

CITIZEN: I demand to be treated with respect, and I insist on being let in. Me and this stadium go way back, we've got history... I survived the terrace collapse back in the Noughties. I've seen all sorts over the years and seasons, and I've come through it all, so I deserve a little respect... I remember when...

STEWARD 2: None of that makes you untouchable, some kind of club legend.

STEWARD 1: I wouldn't let you in even if you put a cornbread vendor's uniform on and said you were going to sell *chipa* in the stands. You're not coming in, and that's the end of it.

CITIZEN: ...the great victories I've seen in this stadium, the glories, league championships, and even way before all that, this place had history: it was here they gathered the recruits who'd enlisted for the Chaco War.*

STEWARD 2: Look, Grandpa... The days of leagues and cups have gone, we've moved on from all that. Besides, it's not even the same stadium: it's been totally remodelled by a consortium of businessmen, authorised by the SS.

CITIZEN: The SS? The Nazis?

STEWARD 1: Didn't you see the 3-D digital display when you came in? The SS: *Su Señoria!*... The Supreme Secretariat! You're going senile; don't you understand abbreviations... initials?

STEWARD 2: Evidently not. The only things he understands are bygone eras and past centuries...

CITIZEN: Well, this stadium has obviously become a circus... a stage for clowns, gags for goals and stunts for strikers, you might say. Playing the joker's clearly your game.

STEWARD 2: It would be better if you left now, old boy, go watch the game at home, eh?...

STEWARD 1: Go on, get going.

CITIZEN: I can't watch it at home: I don't have the access code for the broadcasts.

STEWARD 2: My heart bleeds... That's what happens when you don't keep your credit rating in check and buy in advance.

STEWARD 1: That's how you get stung, you old duffer. Ha! What an idiot!

---

* Estadio Defensores del Chaco (Defenders of El Chaco Stadium), built at the beginnings of the twentieth century in the Sajonia neighbourhood of Paraguay's capital, Asunción, was used for league and cup finals for more than a century, until a larger stadium was constructed in the suburbs. The Defenders of El Chaco Stadium was completely refurbished ahead of its privatisation in 2050.

CITIZEN: I hope you get stung – by a *pikator*!*

STEWARD 2: What d'you just say, you old git?

CITIZEN: *Japoína!* Fuck you... You lot make me sick!

STEWARD 1: Say that again, you stupid old codger. And then see what happens...

CITIZEN: I've nothing else to say. Just that they should rename the Defenders of El Chaco the Pretenders of El Fiasco.

---

* It's said that the *pikator* mosquito bites and bites insistently, and that given its recent proliferation, it can transmit many things, in manifest combinations, way beyond simple dengue fever. It is considered the most macho of Paraguayan mosquitoes.

Diego Trelles Paz (Lima, Peru, 1977) is the author of *Hudson el redentor* (Peru, 2001), *El círculo de los escritores asesinos* (2005) and *Bioy* (2012), which received the Francisco Casavella Prize and was a finalist for the Rómulo Gallegos Prize in 2013. He is also the editor of *El futuro no es nuestro* (2009), an anthology of short stories by young Latin American writers that has been published in six countries and translated into Hungarian and English: *The Future Is Not Ours: New Latin American Fiction* (2012). He holds a doctorate in Hispanic Literature from the University of Texas, Austin, and currently lives in Paris.

'Football and Plague' ('*La peste y el fútbol*') was first published in *Hudson el redentor*.

FOOTBALL AND PLAGUE

Diego Trelles Paz

Translated by Jethro Soutar

> *"He was like Peru, Zavalita, he fucked himself up somewhere down the line. The question is: when?"*
>
> *Conversation in the Cathedral*
> MARIO VARGAS LLOSA

I asked Marcial to tell me a story. He goes back and forth and round and round in circles, telling me to calm down, but no story. Marcial tells a good story. When I was eighteen and still a footballer, Marcial was my teacher on an IT training course for players who hadn't finished high school. It was a three-month course, some place downtown, sponsored by La U. It was a total farce. As soon as the sports papers published photos of us sitting in front of our computers, the coach ordered us to quit...

...to be honest, I wasn't that bothered. I don't think anyone was that bothered. Not even Marcial, who never took us seriously and barely knew how to switch the machines on himself. He made it clear right from the start that he was an Alianza Lima fan, "the people's team". I don't support Alianza or La U. I support Carlos Manucci, a team from Trujillo, my hometown. I've supported them my whole life, they were the team I first played for professionally...

...So what's the point in remembering all this now? There is no point. Everything's pointless when you know you're going to die.

Marcial tries to deny it, shakes his head, says I'm being stupid. He has that knack of being able to cheer you up even though everything's fucked, to make you believe the most fantastic things, to not lose faith. I became convinced of this a few hours ago, as Murci lay dying on the ground. And it was a few hours ago I realised how good Marcial was at telling stories, that instead of ending up a hoodlum he could have been a writer, a politician, a famous orator. Just as I could have been a great footballer. I could have been celebrating the treble today with my La U teammates. I could have done so many other things, and yet here I am...

(...*Live it like you're there with Radio Ovación. One Peru, on the same wavelength: A-RRI-BA PE-RU! Universitario de Deportes nil, Sporting Cristal nil. We've just got under way here at the Estadio Monumental and, Elejalder, the whole place is on fire. La U, going for the treble in a winner-takes-all title decider – whichever side comes out on top here tonight will be the new league champions. The ground is full to bursting, it's madness on the terraces, a carnival... But look out, here comes Ferrari! He's seen Julinho making a run deep into the La U half, the big black figure of Galliquio comes charging over to close him down and... Ouuuchhh! Oh dear, oh dear!... He took him out like a bulldozer!... Blimey, negro! You can take the boy out of Renovación...*)

"Fucking hell, nigger, why'd you always have to be acting like a goddam nigger?!" says Negro Maldad, before taking a long swig of the mini bottle of anise he has in his shaking hands.

"He's gonna be sent off..."

"Turn this shit off, Murci, it's making me nervous," protests Marcial from the back seat. A revolver rests carefully on his right leg.

"Don't be such a pussy. Pejerrey ain't even here yet..."

(...Look out, The Croupier's got his hand in his pocket, and he wouldn't even pardon the president. Speaking of whom, greetings to The Engineer, no doubt tuned in and listening to us from Japan. Thinking of coming back any time soon, Mr President?...)

"Oh, now that he can, he gives Fuji shit... These spineless fucking bastards," says Murci as the bottle is passed to him.

"If Montesinos hadn't sent half of Lima to their graves, people would never have opened their eyes, I'm telling you!" says Marcial. He raises his voice, flickers his eyelids.

"For fuck's sake, Marcial, don't start with your bullshit now!" José cuts in, all irritable, before taking a generous slug of anise.

(...He's calling John Galliquio over. No? Really? Huh? What?... I can't believe my eyes! I must be seeing things! You've given him an extra life, Arana? You, The Croupier, of all people?...)

"He won't last the match on a yellow card," José says. He sparks up a cigarette with one hand and fondles a pair of knickers with the other, knickers snatched from Laurita's dressing-table drawer. "We were in the Juniors together; he always was a hothead. A hatchet-man and a sore loser. Fucking idiot..."

"Not like you, huh, Mr Footballer?..." says Negro Maldad, smiling. "Captain Marvel, wasn't it? Tell us, what's so fucking marvellous about you, huh? Speak up... You're just another Broncano, but with two eyes instead of one, ha, ha, ha..." Maldad's hysterics go on for some time, and he has the sort of laugh that proves contagious. "You basically liked smoking paste more than you liked playing football, and now you're all fucked up like the rest of us. You get mixed up in this shit to put food on the table, homeboy, or to feed your fucking coca habit?"

(...What did you make of that first attack, Don Vides?
Well, Micky, Jean Ferrari broke forward, but he was all on his own.
Sporting Cristal have started very aggressively, pressing high...
Hold on a moment, Don Vides, because La U are pouring forward!
Look out, here comes Grondona's bald head, he's spotted Maldonado,
Paolo Maldonado's calling for it, he's in acres of space – give him the ball,
Gustavo! The ball goes out to Maldonado, delivered on a plate, thank
you, sir, Maldonado sees Edú, look out, there could be a goal here!...)

"Fuck!"

(...Sporting Cristal are defending desperately, Paolo crosses into the
box, Esidio comes charging in, shooooooooots...
Goal.)

"Gooooal, fucking hell, get in!" José and Murci scream with joy...

(Gooooooooooooooooooooooooooooooooooooooal...   for...
Universitariooooooooooo!...)

"Motherfucker! Goal, Ricardo! Step on it, lad, we'll miss
the second half at this rate!" says Alberto Venero to his son, as
they pass La Ensenada beach, their grey Volvo hurtling along the
Panamericana Sur.

(...Four minutes gone... Didn't I tell you a goal was coming, Elejalder?
It was coming and it came. Eduardo Esidio makes the most of the chance,
firing a left-foot rocket that leaves Leao Butrón rooted to the spot and
gives La U the lead!...)

"You drunk yet, Mr Footballer?" says Negro Maldad, his left hand
forcefully kneading José's leg. A fake smile plays across his fat lips

and toothless gums. "I bet you'd love a pinch of coca to stick up that big fucking conk of yours, huh, Captain Marvel? Get wired so you don't shit your pants?"

"You got a fucking problem, nigger?" José cries, violently shaking himself free. Maldad's eyes nearly pop out of his skull, but José slowly lifts his hand to show the handle of his revolver, fronting up, showing defiance.

(...Esidio, Esidio, Esidio, Esidio, that's right everyone, Esidiooooooooo! Goooooooooooooooooooooal Soooooouuuuuutheeern Corp Peruuuuu: Making copper work for Peru...)

"That's it, Mr Footballer, fuck yeah, show me some balls!" Maldad exclaims, breaking the silence with his laughter. "Miiiiister Footballer..." he sings softly, rocking his head from side to side like a drunken teenager.

"Much more of your bullshit, nigger, and you're going to ruin this whole fucking..." Murci says, but without conviction, the insecurity of the weakest.

"Who the fuck you calling nigger, you Indian piece of shit!" Maldad says, furious, snarling his teeth. "Call me nigger again and I'll kill you, you fucking scum, I swear it on La Sarita, I'll pump your fucking face full of lead!..."

(...Four minutes into the first half and Sporting Cristal are already chasing the game, a pinpoint cross from Maldonado leaves Hidalgo and Huamán stranded and lands at Eduardo Esidio's feet, the goal machine, Mr Goal, and he smashes it left-footed into the back of the net, the master poacher notching up his thirty-fifth goal of the campaign and putting Universitario de Deportes ahead on the score sheet: the Meringues one, Sporting Cristal nil. How do you fight a cold, Elejalder? With Formula 44 tablets, Micky...)

"What's the time?" asks Marcial.

"It's three-thirty, Papa, we'll be there any minute," Ricardito replies, accelerating.

"Five more minutes and Pejerrey's fucked it," says Negro Maldad, turning the volume up on the radio.

...Night has fallen. I know it has because I do, because my body tells me so. My body's like a clock, I can guess the time according to its needs... and I'm never wrong... right now, for example, it must be almost six in the evening, because I haven't had a smoke for exactly three hours and ten minutes... if I could have one wish right now, just one... if God, or whoever, came along and saw me and said, Hey, José, one wish, whatever you want? I'd honestly ask for one last smoke of paste... I've asked Marcial. I said: come on brother, show some pity, buy me a little crack, but he just laughed. He laughed nervously, called me nuts... I don't care, maybe I am nuts, but I want a smoke. For fifty miserable cents everything, absolutely everything, seems less awful... I've thought about it often... Smoke and cease to exist in a matter of seconds, go back to dreaming of the great resurrection... José "Captain Marvel" Lescano, ladies and gentlemen... wave to the stands, nod to the dugout, raise the cream shirt to your lips... back in the newspapers again... one-night stands with football groupies... and the banter, squaring up to opponents who are really your mates... the fucking aggro!...

...Marcial saw me play on television several times... he told me so a few seconds ago, but now he's talking to himself... He's an oddball, Marcial, a loose cannon... I got involved in this shit for the sheer hell of it... but him?... What the fuck is someone like him doing here? I never thought I'd ever see him again, least of all in these circumstances... I had him down as respectable, a first-rate guy, an upstanding citizen, but... now what?... how do you explain such things?... what the fuck happened to this country to make honourable people like him become criminals?...

...and another thing I can't understand is why he doesn't just get the fuck out of here... doesn't he know they'll be after us?... he knows, he must know... he's started talking in a low voice, walking about all over the place... he doesn't seem to care if he steps on Murci's body... it wobbles like a jelly every time he knocks into it... I really don't get it. He suddenly came over all twitchy a few hours ago, before the hijack... They announced on the radio that *Barrantes, better known as Frejolito, former leader of the United Left, has died in Cuba*, and he started panicking... What's Barrantes got to do with us?... I don't know... it's all so strange, so incomprehensible... now he's saying something... he's talking... about his past... his past as a militant, he says... his ideals... when we were young, he says... something about class conscience, about the party and comrades... they sold out, the sons of bitches... I can't make head or tail of it... I go over his words in my head, but I can't make sense of them... he babbles on... I think he's lost the plot, but now he sits down beside me and stares into my eyes, a look of resignation... as if I were already dead...

..."It's like a plague, José," he says, afraid... "A plague," he says again. Then he goes silent and still, his eyes red...

(...Look out, here comes Noriega, the Venezuelan, and he's travelling at full pelt, the black giant Galliquio tries to cut him off... Ouuuchhh!... He got him!... Again, negro?... You're already on a yellow card and, uh-oh, the ref's rushing over and he's got "you're off" written all over his face. Uh-oh, yoooou're... He's off...)

"Did he just send him off?" asks Venero senior, aware of the redundancy of his words.

"Dumb piece of shit!" Ricardito spits out in anger. "What was he fucking thinking?... If Cristal score in the next ten minutes... Fuck... I don't even want to think about it."

"Don't forget our little bet, lad, huh?" The friendly tone disorientates Ricardo: how different his father can sound sometimes! How caring! Yet whenever they have a difference of opinion, he won't give an inch. He's not the perfect father, not by any means, but nor is he a total bastard, especially not to his family. Perhaps it's out of shame. Shame for everything Ricardo had to put up with at university and in the streets after Fujimori fell.

(...John Galliquio's been sent off and La U are down to ten men. All of a sudden things are looking a lot less pretty for the Creams. The whole complexion of the game has changed. Thirty-six minutes gone in the first half and Cristal burst forward...)

"I'm telling you, Ricardito... We'll pull it back now that fucking coon's off."

"It's two-nil, Papa..." is all the teenager can bring himself to say.

Ricardo stares absent-mindedly at the beer advertisements on the side of the motorway, playing back his family history: the financial hardship of his youth, the comfort and excess of later years. How did we get from there to here? Because of Papa. As a journalist, he was a mediocre writer, but he had a knack for scoops and headlines. He was sly too. He knew which doors to knock on. He understood when times were tough and it was best to do as you were told, keep your head down. He knew having principles became a burden if you found yourself out of work or under threat. Alberto Venero never spent long on any one newspaper, but he never lacked for work either. They were still living in the prefab on Calle 6 de Agosto in Jesús María when they got the news that would change their lives. It was a Wednesday in April, 1994, a year before the president's re-election. That was the day Ricardito heard the name for the first time: *La Yuca*. His father said it, then fell about laughing, as if it were some kind of joke. I'm the new editor in chief of *La Yuca*. A sensational-ist tabloid. One of those fifty-cent rags bankrolled by businessmen linked to Fujimori. *La Yuca* used its headlines to discredit anyone who opposed the regime, paving the way for re-election. It was a once-in-a-lifetime opportunity, son, that's all. They were difficult times, I accepted their offer and I think I did the right thing. I did it for you guys, but you don't understand that. You're incapable of putting yourself in my shoes. You're a spoilt brat. Don't raise your voice at me! You ungrateful little runt, how the fuck do you think we could afford university? Without *La Yuca* – listen carefully to what I'm saying – without that bullshit rag of a newspaper, there'd have been no food on the table, never mind the Volvo, the beach house, the little trips to Miami you were so fond of. There'd have been fuck all. Think about that next time you show your father a lack of respect!

"What's with you all deep in thought, Ricardo?" Venero asks suddenly, snapping Ricardo out of his dreamy recollections. "You're away with the fairies, son..."

"Oh, nothing, Papa, nothing..."

(*...Did he take a swing at him, Elejalder? Did he really just sock him one, just like that?... Unbelievable! Carranza, The Puma, has just assaulted Soria. The youngster is laid out flat on the ground. Outrageous! That's a red card if ever I saw one, Mr Arana, and here he comes now, he calls Carranza over, the Cristal players are under-standably livid, and, well, it's good night Carranza...*)

"The kid's landed you in the shit here, Ricardo," Venero says mockingly. "La U are fucked now, son, you've had it..."

(*...But wait a minute... What?! I can't believe it. I won't believe it! Right, that's it. I'm out of here. Who wants to commentate on the rest of*

the game? Elejalder? You want to take the mic, Rolly? How about you,
Don Vides? I can't believe it... Incredible... He's let him off the hook!...
What a disgrace, Arana! I don't want to tell you how to do your job,
Delfino, distinguished members of the FA, but this is scandalous. No,
no, nooo! I'm out of here... Come on, who's gonna commentate?...)

"Hear that? Hear that, son? This ref's a motherfucker!... The
bastard thief!"

"No Papa, not a real thief," Ricardito thinks right away, and
it's as if a lid blows off the pressure cooker inside him. "The real
thieves are the bastards you defend in your newspaper, who are
fleeing the country right now, weighed down with cash. The real
thieves are you and your bosses and your bosses' bosses. And me:
I'm a thief. I, who marched through the streets protesting against
a government that paid my university fees while you spat out lies
in your newspaper."

"Hey, lad, cat got your tongue?... It's half-time, the ref just gifted
you the game and you sit there in silence like an idiot... What's the
matter? What's on your mind, Ricardo? Birds? Studies? The beers
you're gonna have to buy me when Silva starts banging them in?"

"..."

"Hear what I said? The Blind Bat's gonna make changes. He'll
bring Silva on for the second half. He'd better do, anyway!"

"..."

"Hey, Ricardo, are you going to fucking answer me or what?"

"Sorry, Papa. I was thinking about something else."

"Well, keep your shit together, will you, son? Hang on, what are
you doing?... No! I told you not to go through Atocongo, for fuck's
sake! Now look! You've got us slap bang in the middle of a fuck-off
traffic jam – and right in front of some fucking newbuild estate full
of yobs!..."

"It's just a little hold-up, Papa, it'll clear in no time."

"Clear in no time, my ass. We're going to be here for hours: we've fucked it! We'll never make the second half…"

"And everyone in that fucking newbuild estate full of yobs reads your newspaper, Papa."

"Listen, you little shit, don't fucking start with that now!…"

(…Look out, Cristal are piling forward, La U are defending desperately. Ferrari to Soto, Soto to Hidalgo, Hidalgo to Noriega – it's a sky-blue tidal wave. La U, down to ten men, show their teeth, bare their claws, sharpen their nails, cling to their two-nil lead. Five minutes into the second half, ladies and gentlemen, and it's chaos in the Universitario penalty area: there's pushing and shoving and holding. Here comes Julinho with a fierce shot, half-saved by Ibáñez, but Hidalgo pounces on the rebound, hits it full blassssttt….
Goal.)

"Goal, goal, gooooal!" Venero shouts triumphantly, over and over again, sticking his head out the window.

(…Goooooooooooooooooooooal… for… Spoooooooortiiiiiiiiiiiing Criiiiistaaaaaaaaaaaal!)

"Bottled it, ain't they, Mr Footballer?" Maldad's wicked smile appears, quick as a flash. José keeps his mouth shut. A cold sweat breaks out on his face, soaks his back, moistens the palms of his hands. He feels scared for the first time.

(…Didn't I tell you, Elejalder? I said, "Look out, here come the Sky Blues. Look out, this time they mean business." Chaos in Universitario's box, and Martín Hidalgo profits with a fierce left-foot shot that flew past Óscar Ibáñez: there was nothing the keeper could do about it, and Sporting Cristal reduce the deficit with six minutes gone in the second half…)

"You see?... See what happens when you make me angry and start up with your bullshit... Look son, I don't want to drag this argument out and spoil your mother's evening at home... Let's call it quits, huh? What do you say, champ?"

(...Hidalgo, Hidalgo, Hidalgo... Hidaaaaaaaaaaalgoooooooooo! Meeeeeboooooooocaaaaaaíííííínaaaaaa: Soothes coughs and sore throats...)

"Sure, Papa... Sorry..."

"Two-one, dumbass... Two-one and the equaliser's on its way... Silva still hasn't scored yet. When Silva scores, then I'll forgive you."

"Want me to take Tomás Marsano?"

"What other way is there to take?..."

"Aviación?"

"No, just take Marsano, I don't want to end up in another fucking jam... I hope we don't bring Waldir on."

"Waldir will definitely come on, Papa, he always does."

"I hope to God he doesn't, Ricardo. That black bastard has fucking shit for brains."

...Cold... I feel ice cold, and yet I'm sweating like a pig... like a pig, and I'm shaking... I don't know how to explain it... it's an icy sweat, that's it... icy... as if something is leaving me and... I'm afraid... I've thought about death before, but now... I can't get my breath, I'm in shock... Do I deserve to die?... what difference does it make, we're all going to die anyway... best to think about something else... I want to play the scene over again in my head, but I can't make out the images... and I'm starting to get delirious... there's a shoot-out... I'm on the ground, with this hole in my stomach... I hear the boy suddenly scream, he falls... a sudden buzzing... a puddle of black blood, growing quickly... I don't even know who the fuck

shot who... I don't even know who shot me... or Negro Maldad...
I saw him lying dead in the car... and now my conscience... fuck...
what should I think about?... Renzo? Think about my son, or my
sister?... what for?... better not; better they don't know about any
of this... poor lad, poor little Renzito... life will gobble him up too...
and Marcial... it's as if he's gone stupid, Marcial... lost, resigned...
like the rest of us...

*(...But what's Waldir doing over there? Too late, the former Alianza
striker is much too slow. He looks lost out there to me, totally off the
pace, wouldn't you agree, Rolly? Waldir, do you want to play for
Cristal or what?...)*

"It's four-thirty, Negro! Where the fuck is Pejerrey?"

"See, Papa? Waldir did come on and he's started fucking everything up already..."

"Just step on it, Ricardo, less of the smart talk, I want to get
there today, OK?"

"He has to pass by this way... He'll be here any moment..."

"Bull-fucking-shit he'll be here any moment! Does he even go
this way? Are you fucking us around?"

"Footballer... I'm going to fucking well kill you..."

"Your mother will be cursing us by now, son, I'm telling you..."

"There they are! Step on it!"

(...Well, Micky, one thing's for sure...
*Did you see that, Don Vides? Did you just see that? Waldir gets
hold of the ball in the middle of the park and brainlessly gives it straight
back again...)*

"Ricardo! Look out!" The old Toyota comes flying out of a side
street onto Avenida Parque Sur and blocks them off. Ricardo slams

on the brakes to try and avoid the collision. The radio blares out from both cars. The hoodlums surround the Volvo, their shouting blending with the voices of the commentators.

(...and now Portilla has it, the black figure of Giuliano Portilla bursts forward...)

"Move and I'll blow your fucking head off!" screams Murci, as he approaches the door to the passenger seat, his revolver trained on Venero.

"Open the door, Murci!" cries Marcial, a few feet behind. Neither of them can read Venero's intentions: he stares back at them blankly, keeping his cool. In fact he already has his left hand on the gun he keeps under the car seat. "It's OK, son. Keep still and stay in the car. When I get out, lean forward and cover your head with your arms, OK? Everything's going to be fine," says Venero in a whisper. He moves so fast it's difficult to establish the proper order of events. But whether the door is opened by Murci or Venero himself doesn't really matter: what matters is that Venero hits his target with both his two shots, though unfortunately for him he doesn't kill anyone; Murci and José both fall, struck down but alive.

"Papaaaaa!" shouts Ricardito, terrified, doing exactly the opposite of what his father instructed.

(...he looks up, there's no one to pass it to, he can't see a teammate anywhere...)

"Ricardo, noooooo, soooooooon!..." Venero's anguished cry comes at the same moment his head is flipped round by a thunderous gunshot. The last image he will see in life will be that of his son staring back at him, not knowing why his legs are giving way and why he's losing his balance. It's impossible to tell who shot them.

Laid out on the ground, José figures it must have been Maldad, but then he remembers El Negro has been dead in the car for several minutes.

(...he's completely on his own, he looks up again, thinks about hitting one from thirty yards, he shoooooooooooots...)

"Undercover agents, Marcial! Come on, fucking hell!" Murci yells from the back seat, a trail of fresh blood painting his wayward route to the Toyota.

(What a goal!
Goooooooooooooooooooooooooal...   for...
Universitaariooooooooooooooo!)

"Marciaaaal! Don't leave me!" José cries desperately, his battered body lying prone in the road. He can't move. Marcial's fat hands scoop him up and dump him on the back seat next to Murci. The car speeds away. José notices that Murci is vomiting blood. Before passing out, the cry of "goal" from the car's speakers draws a faint smile on his pained face.

(...Ohhhhhhhhh!!! Myyyyyyyyyy!!! Gooooooood!!! What an unbe-lievable goal the boy just scored! He pounced on a terrible mistake by Waldir Sáenz, caught trying to dribble down a blind alley, and all on his own, when no one was expecting it, with Cristal seemingly about to get the equaliser, Portilla lets fly with a bullet from outside the box that flies past Leao, who can't believe his eyes. It's the goal of the treble! It's the goal of the century! The goal that, thirty-nine minutes into the second half, with six minutes left to play, sets Universitario de Deportes on the way to becoming, for the first time in their history, Peruvian league champions for the third consecutive season...)

"Oh God! Help! Somebody do something!"

"Call an ambulance, someone, quick!"

"An ambulance, for God's sake, there are people dying here!"

(...What's for dinner tonight, Elejalder?... Hilton chicken and a mixed grill, Micky: delicious!...)

...Marcial... he's talking again... saying absurd things... he's crying... I can no longer feel anything... not pain... not pity... not bitterness... just a lack of breath... Marcial is finally telling a story... the last one... the most illogical one of all... about bullets... two bullets... he says... and he smiles, sadly... we're not bad men, José... but it's all so pointless... I shot Maldad... he says... the kidnap never existed... it was a set-up right from the start... they wanted Venero dead... he knew too much... they needed people to blame... he says... El Negro was in on it... Venero saved him a job... we slaughter ourselves... that's why I killed him... he says... I can't prove it... I don't want to prove it... it doesn't matter... either way, he's dead... I don't feel bad... sirens can be heard... and the mechanical click of his revolver... two bullets left... he says again... and he stretches out a hand towards me... I feel the coldness of the barrel on my head... it's as if he were combing my hair... we'll suffer less from now on... he says...

Vinicius Jatobá was selected by *Granta* as one of the Best of Young Brazilian Novelists in 2012. Since then he has had stories published in English, French, Spanish and German. He is also a prize-winning dramatist. In 2015 he'll be in Paris for a year as the recipient of the prestigious Icatu Prize for Arts, where he'll work on his new novel, *Enchantment Road*. His first novel, *Elegy*, will be published in early 2015.

'The Big Family' ('*A grande família*') was written especially for *The Football Crónicas* and is published here for the first time.

THE BIG FAMILY

Vinicius Jatobá

Translated by Jethro Soutar

Boys and girls, I'm going to tell you an old port story, and it's one of the noblest adventures mankind has undertaken since he came down from the trees and quit monkeying around in paradise, said Tio Balela. It's a football story, a tale of two halves. And it's a love story. We bounced up and down, we pushed and we shoved and we sat our bums down on the living-room floor, Nicinho elbowing his way to the best spot, irking Seu Bahia, who said behave yourself lad, someone needs to teach that rascal some manners, and Tio Balela said leave him be, he's fresh off the baby's bottle, but he can see life's a swindle, that you get more from biting than from biding, and anyway, there's no harm in a bit of play-fighting among cousins, he'll grow up to be a man with a boxed ear and thick skin, and he'll learn to sleep with one eye open, and that's the way it should be. Then Tio Balela closed his eyes and took a deep breath, and he stayed like that for a while, waiting for the spark, and Felipinho, Garito and Joínha sat goggle-eyed, staring at his mouth, the better to hear the story when it finally came out, and Tio Balela just sat there chewing his mouth and smiling. And then he spoke.

I've heard the story told many times, said Tio Balela, by Seu Nino, who was told it by his father, Old Abrão, who was told it by his father, Young Abrão, who was known as Boy Abrão in the fish and tobacco stores on Rua do Acre, where he whiled away his afternoons, a drunken bum, his chit-chat dripping with nostalgia for the ugly foreign land he'd left behind. He'd tell tall tales to whoever would listen, and I only ever listened because I liked Dona Samanta's cakes, for as Seu Bahia will tell you, I can't stand lies and I come out in a rash whenever anyone spins me a yarn; I'm very scientific when it comes to stories. But that old devil Young Abrão had a certain charm about him, said Tio Balela, and although I had to discount a lot of what he said before I finally heard a story I could believe in, I did believe this one, and not because Young Abrão crossed his heart and hoped to die – he'd have been long dead and buried if that were the case, for the old guy may have been an atheist, but he liked swearing on the holiest of holies that his extravagant stories were true. I believed this story, which I first heard while eating one of Dona Samanta's fondants, said Tio Balela, because Old Abrão didn't blink when I had him confirm the story later, and he said exactly the same thing his father had said, as if reciting his times tables, and Seu Nino didn't scratch his nose when I had him reconfirm the story even later, and he too said the same thing his father had said, as if reciting his times tables, and every fibber has a nervous trait, and I knew all their ticks and they were tickless when they spoke. So I believed them.

According to what Seu Nino said his father used to say, said Tio Balela, it all began when Young Abrão witnessed a miracle with his two blue eyes, eyes that have long since been swallowed up by the earth, and the miracle only changed in its telling in that sometimes it was raining and sometimes it was sunny, sometimes the sea was calm and sometimes it devoured everything in its wake, because Young Abrão would vary things to suit his audience. But the facts never changed, said Tio Balela, for facts are facts, and what happened was a fact and will remain a fact until the end of time. Young Abrão was sitting on a bench at Praia Formosa, looking to the horizon and drinking a beer, when a boy, a boy so skinny as a rake he could have dodged the wind, leapt six feet in the air and walloped a little coconut with his right-foot so hard, but so incredibly hard, that all the seagulls took flight and what was left of the coconut flew out to sea and doubtless came to rest in Sergipe, unless it smashed into the hull of a ship on the way and caused some kind of disaster. The setting for this miracle was the much-missed Ponte dos Marinheiros, and Young Abrão peered down from the bridge at the kid lying in the sand, smiling up into the bright blue sky, and Young Abrão saw in that boy's face – saw, appreciated and marvelled – the roots that made Brazil white, black and Indian, white-black, black-Indian and Indian-white, all in the same family.

The skinny-as-a-rake boy playing in the sand was a Da Silva, a Da Silva like Bahia is a Da Silva, and Nicinho is a Da Silva, and Garito is a Da Silva, and Joínha is a Da Silva, and Felipe is a Da Silva, and it's said that every Da Silva is born with a certain charm, said Tio Balela. There are Da Silvas who make tiles and Da Silvas who deliver letters, and there are Da Silvas who make bread and Da Silvas who grind stone, and there's a Da Silva for every day of the week and hour of the day and star in the sky, and one day there'll be a president Da Silva, and an astronaut Da Silva in space. Young Abrão used to say that the Da Silva he saw on the beach must have been born with one foot in a beehive, there was so much sweetness, honey and nectar in that boy's foot, and indeed he was right, for that skinny-as-a-rake boy was none other than Leônidas Diamante Negro, our immortal footballing poet, favourite son of the city's waterfront neighbourhoods, the city that was São Sebastião do Rio de Janeiro, a city that mindlessly cemented and pebbled over the beach and bridge where its prodigal son had been born, although the son found it in his heart to forgive this terrible vandalism, for sons always forgive the clumsy love of their parents, said Tio Balela.

Young Abrão was only young, said Tio Balela, but he foresaw what was going to happen: that skinny-as-a-rake boy was going to make the whole mixed-up country shout the same name and share the same passion. And this was the 1920s, a different time, a bygone era, when I was just a nipper back in Sertânia and had never even dreamt of living in this city of ours. But people don't dream of Rio, said Tio Balela, Rio dreams of people, and once the city's chosen you there's nothing you can do but climb into the mermaid's bed and let yourself be entrapped, caressed and charmed, oblivious to what's happening because you're absent, distant and stupefied, until sooner or later you dock here, because it's inevitable. That's the way it was with me, the way it was with Seu Bahia, and according to Seu Nino, the way it was with his grandfather, that much-missed old devil Young Abrão. He arrived in port on board the *Queen Mary*, with his *gringo* cohorts and a leather ball under his arm, and they had the same fancy, pompous surnames noblemen here wore like medals, but despite their funny way of talking, their light-coloured eyes and their freckles, they weren't well-heeled and they weren't allowed to kick a ball about in the palm-tree-lined fields of Laranjeiras and Botafogo. They were what they were, and ports are the same everywhere, in heaven and in hell.

As Seu Nino said Young Abrão told Old Abrão, they may have had fancy, pompous surnames, but they were the Da Silvas of England and the Scotlands, and they may have been as pasty-white as the make-up-clad toffs who gathered in Rio's society clubs, but they didn't wear cravats to play a kick-and-run all full of rules and regulations, said Tio Balela. We waterfront and suburbs people were the underclass back then, said Tio Balela. You kids will prove things are different today, but back then people of our ilk were either in jail or constantly dodging the police – who roamed the streets on the look-out for vagrants, like slave-hunters of old – or else polishing or sweeping or welding or hammering or carrying the lord of the manner's booty on their sweaty backs, for there's a lot to smile about in this world, lots to dance for and to like, but it can be a slog too, and for every man who smiles over his filet mignon, there's a hundred weep into their brisket. The visitors from England were an underclass with lighter skins, an underclass like us but that slept in barrels of holy water, for they too polished, swept and welded, said Tio Balela, and they had backs covered in calluses like we did, for they were Da Silva Smitis and Jaimis and Tompisons. They were our brothers.

As soon as they set foot and ball in Saúde and Gamboa, they were welcomed like the crack players they were, said Tio Balela. They won everywhere they played and they played everywhere they went, wherever they found five, six, seven able-bodied men and a patch of ground to get the ball rolling. According to Seu Nino, said Tio Balela, they played on the Cleto and Damião quays, on the Pedra do Sal, at the Bragança shipyard, inside the Fluminense mill, even on the Mineiros wharf. And according to Young Abrão, who told Seu Nino, and Old Abrão later confirmed it, every game was a walkover, and every clear goal the *gringos* won by was worth a beer from the nearest grocer's, and once it was such a thrashing that the *gringos* guzzled thirty gulps of Argentinian wine, with one of them so half-cut he started chewing a segment of ball thinking it was tobacco. One clear sunny day, the fearsome battalion privates of the marine infantry came down from the Ilha das Cobras, said Tio Balela, and the only defeat in the entire history of the battalion came that day against the *gringos*. But according to Seu Nino, even in defeat the privates were happy, said Tio Balela, and they spilt out around Ilha dos Melões, blacks and whites together in a tidal wave of smiles, as noisy as a capoeira gang.

And eventually what happened, as always happens, for a port is a place of comings and goings, is that the time came for the *Queen Mary* to go, and it disappeared over the horizon. But a little while later, it was as if it were still at dock, for the number of blond-haired boys and blue-eyed mulatto kids who appeared shortly thereafter was amazing, all of them born in the same few weeks and by the same midwife, Euzébia, said Tio Balela. And according to Seu Nino,

Young Abrão would say to his son, Old Abrão, it's just mental arithmetic: if a boy runs kind of jerky and has a good shot on him and catches fish with hardly any bait on his hook, he has to be the son of Merle Loide, the *gringos*' fun-loving captain, a man who was such a bag of tricks that he kicked with his hand and headed with his foot and everyone still thought it delightful and clapped. And Young Abrão would say that, furthermore, the lad Rasteiro, who borrows passengers' wallets on the Valongo tram without asking, once did so many keepy-uppies that the story Jurema, his mother, told about his having blue eyes on account of her eating so many grapes during pregnancy had to be revised, for Rasteiro could only be the son of Jomaguil, who, according to what Old Abrão told Seu Nino, once travelled from England to France doing kick-ups on deck and didn't let the ball fall once, not even in a rainstorm, a feat that made headlines in maritime union newspapers on both sides of the Channel.

The *Queen Mary*'s sons and daughters began to accumulate and multiply, and it was as if Old Abrão, who was still young back then, was guardian to all of them, for his house on Rua Jogo da Bola was always full of kids. And Young Abrão said to his son Old Abrão, he who loves the city stays in the city, and some people love just a part of the city and that's enough reason for them to stay. The part that Young Abrão loved, said Tio Balela, had a naughty smile, soft lips and a generous lap; she was the colour of cocoa, mother to Old Abrão, grandmother to Seu Nino, princess and queen to Young Abrão, whom she only ever called boy, Boy Abrão, and by the time I met her she was an old lady, who sold cakes, and the pearl that was Samanta had become Dona Samanta, out of respect and propriety, and her delicacies were so legendary they filled throats such as that of Jaime Mocoso, the honey-toned cherub who sang in the Rádio Nacional choir and earned a bit of extra shrapnel performing serenades to the betrothed maidens of Botafogo and Laranjeiras noblemen.

Young Abrão never won on the lottery, nor did he have any luck in the Largo da Prainha church bingo, said Tio Balela. If he said it was going to rain the sun would shine, and if he chose to wear a coat it would turn out to be a scorcher. That was Young Abrão. But one day he was sitting outside a grocery store in Gamboa and saw the same dark-skinned skinny-as-a-rake boy from the beach whizz by on a bicycle with a food delivery, and Young Abrão felt in his bones that same sense of certainty he'd felt on Formosa beach. He stood up proudly and proclaimed, pointing at the boy who was by now way out of sight, that kid's gonna grow up to be the next Isabelino Gradín, and Mário Soares Azevedo, a nimble Portuguese who made English leather shoes on Rua Sete de Setembro, asked whether Mister Iungui was really asking whether that boy would be the next lackey or the next dunce, and before the laughter of the lettered men present, Young Abrão said what I'm really saying, Seu Soares, is that the boy will become a king, for the prince already exists, and that's Gradín, and anyone who can't see that doesn't have his head screwed on. And Seu Soares burst out laughing, scratched his whiskers and said to Young Abrão charitably, when is that big heart of yours going to realise that Brazil is a shipwreck, Mister Iungui, that having all these awful creoles tied to our feet is holding back our development, our nation. This country has a future, Mister Iungui, but first it has to free itself of its baggage, its dead weights, the blight that is the inheritance of people of colour. And Seu Soares turned to receive the admiring looks and nods of the learned men he shared a table with.

And now, Seu Soares went on, you've got that imbecile Gradín giving the rabble ideas, the rabble that never amounts to anything and never will, the Uruguayans should be ashamed of themselves, this feud they're starting, making trouble for their neighbours, creating problems and agitating, for as any gentleman knows, it's cruel to let an ass think he might become a stallion, because an ass is an ass, a pleb is a pleb and Zé Povinho is Zé Povinho. Then Seu Soares got up and paid for his coffee and the gentlemen with him got up too and Seu Soares came over and stretched out a hand to Young Abrão and said in a kindly voice, am I right or am I right, Mister Iungui, and Young Abrão's reply still echoes in the hearts of brickmakers, stonemasons, firemen, tram conductors, deliverymen, fishermen, engine drivers, stokers, crane operators, longshoremen and checking clerks today: Seu Soares, my name is Abrão Young, and I can't be friends with anyone who's not friends with my friends. The whole grocery store broke out in thunderous applause, said Tio Balela, and Seu Soares left the store feeling snubbed, his colleagues frightened and speaking in whispers. Laughter erupted and the owner of the establishment, Seu Ernani, said, I know who you're talking about, Young Abrão, that skinny boy's the son of Maria by birth and Mario by default, and Seu Manoel Nunes who died was from the port and he was an honourable man. He's a good lad that lad, and sir's totally right: the ball just loves his feet.

At first Young Abrão was the only one aware of it, until one became two when Seu Ernani had cottoned on. He and Young Abrão would lurk together in the stands at São Cristóvão, admiring the way the lad Leônidas, no longer such a rake, moved about the pitch so majestically, parading past other boys with the ball, said Tio Balela. And Boy Abrão told me, sitting in his rocking chair on Rua do Acre one day, that two became seven, and twelve became fifty-three, and two hundred and eighty-five became one thousand six hundred and ninety-four, until there were no fingers on hands and toes on feet left to count all the adoring eyes that watched, mesmerised, etching the young crack's every movement on their memories. Seu Nino said Young Abrão used to say that Fluminense had fans, that Bangu had fans, that Bonsucesso had fans and that América had fans, but with Leônidas it was different, said Tio Balela, because the noisy mob that followed him around, hugging euphorically like devotees before the cardinal, clapping and jumping like deranged goats whenever he let fly with a brilliant shot, weren't mere fans, they couldn't be, said Tio Balela, for what they were, what that bedlam really was, was a big family.

When the good ship *Arlanza,* huge and elegant, left the port of Rio de Janeiro, making happy whistles and pregnant whale snorts, bound for the World Cup and the bygone France of 1938, and of this myself and Seu Bahia bore witness, the big family Young Abrão had foreseen on Formosa beach all those years ago had grown too big to fit on the Mauá quayside. There were so many people jumping up and down at the same time it might have caused an earthquake in Japan, said Tio Balela, and there were all sorts in that excitable family, the pretty and the ugly, the sour and the sweet, the blue-collared and the white-collared, those who spoke with plums in their mouths and those who had no teeth, and some people swear that in the committee of honour his excellency, his highness, his greatness, the president, Getúlio Vargas, whined like a weaning calf, a rosary clutched in one hand, willing Leônidas and the rest of the golden boys to come back with proof of what we all knew to be true, said Tio Balela, a truth that wasn't written down in grammar and arithmetic books but that could be smelt in the air, across oceans and continents: that we may not have invented football, but we had become its master.

Yet on that very same day, another momentous event took place in the port, said Tio Balela. Only a few stray cats remained, staring aimlessly at the sea, for the *Alanza* had long since disappeared from human sight, but there they remained, and they had good reason to. A great, important, impelling reason to. People began to hurry back as soon as they heard the rumour, and anyone unfamiliar with the port's past capers hurried back as soon as they'd been brought up to speed. The stray cats on the quayside turned their heads as one, said Tio Balela, in amazement and excitement, because there in the customs quarantine, awaiting authorisation to dock, was the

Queen Mary, exactly three decades since its last visit had caused such a commotion.

Young Abrão was lying in his hammock when word of the unlikely visit reached him via his neighbours, but he didn't believe it, for as any old sailor knows, the only thing that brings back long-lost ships is the midday sun. But then the boy Policarpo arrived panting at the door, flapping his skinny little arms and yelping, Seu Young Abrão, your presence is required down in the square, and Young Abrão asked, is it a matter of sea or land, and the boy said, it's a sea matter, Seu Abrão, and Young Abrão knew the boy Policarpo wouldn't lie. So Young Abrão made his way down the Conceição hillside as best he could, said Tio Balela, for by then he was never without his trusty walking stick, and he crossed Praça Mauá at a fair clip and sidled up to the crowd of curious onlookers. He peered through his binoculars and, so Seu Nino told me, a big smile lit up his face when he saw Merle Loide standing on the starboard side, head full of white hair but still very much the captain, a ball under one arm, cheeks swollen from all the cognac he'd guzzled.

They'd brought a ball and they'd brought crack players too, so it was said, but this time things would be different, so it was also said, by every tongue in every local's mouth. In grocery stores, bars and quaysides, in factories, brickworks and quarries, atop mules and under them too, as Seu Nino would say, there came the same message, and me and Seu Bahia heard it from mouthwashed mouths just as we did from wino mouths, and it was this: if those *gringos* thought they could give us another beating with their tame little shots they had another think coming; if they knew what was good for them they'd disappear back up their gangway and make for the high seas, full steam ahead. In billiard rooms and snooker halls, in between rounds of spoof and laying bets on the numbers game, over assembly lines and clothes lines, all anyone talked about was the game, the game that should take place and would take place, and the team line-up that began to be shrewdly devised. Two runners, Girino and Fradinho, as full-backs, Seu Bahia, as strong as Domingos da Guia, at centre-half. Sebastião Lourenço, a half-blind accountant from the Vapor Quay, who was hopeless at counting centavos but could pick a pass at fifty yards, as a half-back. The boy Rasteiro, keepy-uppy champ and a boy no more, at outside-left, and the ball-playing offspring of Merle Loide alongside him in the forward line. No sooner had Jaime Mocoso been thought of than he showed up singing a waltz, and Madame Leila Buriti agreed not to wear a dress and not to speak so high-pitched, but said he'd only play if he was still allowed to wear make-up, and he was, and so it was settled. Selection continued, said Tio Balela, crack players summoned one by one as a waterfront dream team began to form.

Until there were just two places left, said Tio Balela.

Roncador was woken by Comandante Brito in his prison cell on Ilha das Cobras, and Comandante Brito asked Roncador if by any chance he liked Vargas, and Roncador said, no, he didn't like him, and Comandante Brito asked Roncador if by any chance he'd like to give Vargas a kiss, and Roncador said, forgive me, Comandante Brito, but no, he wouldn't like to give Vargas a kiss, he'd more likely give that cuckold a kick, and Comandante Brito asked Roncador if by any chance he believed in God and Providence, and Roncador said, forgive me such an affront, Comandante Brito, but no, I'm not a believer, for I'm an anarchist, and Comandante Brito said, an anarchist, how charming, does that thick head of yours have no shame? Then Comandante Brito scratched his beard and asked Roncador if by any chance he believed in the ball, and Roncador said, my dear Comandante Brito, I pray to the ball every God-damned day, for it is the most divine thing that has ever been and will ever be created, from the beginning of time until the end of the world, and Comandante Brito said, in that case, Roncador, consider your esteemed self selected for the mighty port team that will give those *gringo* jokers from the *Queen Mary* a hiding in five days' time, and Roncador said a happy, yes, sir, Comandante Brito, you can count on me.

Which meant there was just one place left, said Tio Balela.

But it was difficult to get hold of Evandro da Silva Berto, for Evandro da Silva Berto didn't exist. If you went to Gamboa and asked for Evandro, nobody would have heard of him, and if you went to Estácio and asked for Evandro, nobody would have heard of him there either, just as they wouldn't have in Saúde, Santo Cristo or Caju. But if you asked for Cinco Pernadas, the brave would break out in a cold sweat, maidens would shiver in shame, and the lettered would open their wallets, said Tio Balela. For he who was born Evandro da Silva Berto was rechristened when young, after being set upon by a throng of cowardly police in Praça XV and letting fly with a capoeira roundhouse and a half-moon, taking out eight policemen in two swoops, hence Quatro Pernadas, the four-legged kid. While still a boy he collected debts, he bodyguarded candidates for office and he minded entrances to grocery stores, said Tio Balela, for he was brave, fearless and feared, and though he still only had bumfluff for a beard, he had the respect of the toughest ex-cons on the street.

Evandro da Silva Berto made the leap from four legs to five after he went to work at the Gênova cabaret and the lovely girls there fought and scratched over the right to have him as their protector, said Tio Balela, but it became enshrined in legend after he was stabbed fifteen times in an ambush attack one moonless night in the dark shadows of the Canal do Mangue, and was then seen the very next day dancing with six mulattas at Estácio as if nothing had happened, not a scratch on him, his smile as bright as ever, his voice still small for such a man mountain. There were those who didn't believe what had happened and those who did and set to prayer, and those who weren't sure but were shit-scared either way. What there wasn't was anyone who dared go near him after that.

So if even Vargas couldn't track Cinco Pernadas down, said Tio Balela, and Vargas had the whole police and army and Church at his disposal, how could anyone else be expected to find the rascal in whatever corner he skulked in? It was impossible, and it went on being impossible for three days, until I was drinking with Seu Bahia and Girino and Elídio and Macau and Fradinho and Jurubeba and Japonês Anastácio, and Cinco Pernadas suddenly just appeared, in flesh and blood, blown in on the wind, and he says, good afternoon, gentlemen, a little bird tells me Seu Young Abrão wants to talk to me, and I said, yes, that's true, we've been looking for you everywhere, Seu Cinco Pernadas, and Cinco Pernadas said, it doesn't bode well to be findable, people only find me when I want to be found, and if I go looking for someone, it bodes ill for them to be findable too, for I'm not in the habit of scouring the streets, looking for people. Then he sat down to find out what it was all about, and he was told in detail what it was about and he smiled, for it would be his pleasure to let his five legs loose on the *gringos*.

And thus the line-up for the mighty port team was signed and shaken on, said Tio Balela.

Back then, Old Abrão was still a nipper, but he remembered a lot, said Tio Balela, things he told me and things he told his son, Seu Nino, and that Seu Nino then told me. And Old Abrão's most cherished memory was not breaking into the Cemitério dos Ingleses to eat *jabuticabas* and mess around, much less of skiving off school to listen to Jaime Mocoso record songs at the Rádio Nacional studios. No, his most cherished childhood memory was seeing Young Abrão and Merle Loide embrace when they were finally reunited after the *Queen Mary* had spent three long days at sea, awaiting authorisation. Old Abrão told me, and I repeat it now for the benefit of you kids, that the friendship between Young Abrão and Merle Loide was true friendship, and in that embrace Old Abrão's father found all that he'd left behind in English and Scottish lands, lands he only visited in dreams. If I close my eyes and let my mind wander, said Tio Balela, it wanders back to the door of my house in Sertânia, just like one day you'll all remember running riot around the streets of Vaz Lobo, Irajá and Vicente de Carvalho, for everyone has a sense of nostalgia, and it's good to have one, and the older you get the more you live in it.

Young Abrão and Merle Loide sat down and they started chatting as if not a day had gone by, never mind thirty years, since Young Abrão had decided to stay put on Carioca soil. Young Abrão and Merle Loide sat there and they drank, Old Abrão told Seu Nino, said Tio Balela, and there they remained, chattering away in that silly language of theirs, and all the *Queen Mary*'s offspring sat around listening to them, though they couldn't understand a peep, and they laughed when Young Abrão and Merle Loide laughed, and they cried when Young Abrão and Merle Loide cried. And Old Abrão said that when they cried it was beautiful: Merle Loide took out a silk-cloth bundle and inside was the tattered cap that used to go on Kelvin Leite's bald head and the wooden pipe that used to go in Kelvin Leite's toothless mouth, and Kelvin Leite was Young Abrão's father, Old Abrão's grandfather, Seu Nino's great-grandfather, and Young Abrão and Merle Loide fell silent. They looked out upon the distant city, for they were at the top of Conceição hill, and then Merle Loide muttered something in his language and Young Abrão said, yes, there'll be a match, it was all set.

And all set it was, said Tio Balela. The crowd piled in around the São Cristóvão pitch and there were police and firemen, bacchanal experts and moonshine connoisseurs, employers and employees, handymen of every sort, pretty girls with cavityless smiles and a multitude of delicacies from Canal do Mangue and Ilhas dos Melões, said Tio Balela. The crowd was already in a frenzy, for over in France, Brazil had beaten Poland in a six-five thriller, Leônidas scoring a hat-trick, and so it was madness in the stands, more like a

Deixa Falar carnival ball than a football match. The *gringos* laughed and savoured every minute of the non-stop party, and silence only descended when Padre Macedo from the Largo da Prainha church came onto the pitch to say some nice words about love and peace and brotherhood, and he closed his Bible and everyone clapped and then he sat down on the port team's substitutes' bench, for the hallowed priest was our intrepid coach.

Lining up to represent the port was the best team in all the world, players who have gone down in folklore and are still talked about today. There was Seu Bahia and Girino and Fradinho and Sebastião Lourenço and Jaime Mocoso, who sang the national anthem in tears, and Madame Leila Buriti in shorts and shirt but with a rosy-pink mouth, and there was Rasteiro, his hair standing on end like a drowned rat, and Lero, Raposo and Mascate, Meire Lorde's three sons from three different port beauties. There was Japonês Anastácio, who couldn't shoot for toffee but was good in the air, Severo Augusto Matraca Leocácio, fugitive leader of the dockers' union, who Comandante Brito pretended not to recognise, and whenever someone told him it was the much-feared Matraca he'd tell them to wash their mouths out with soapy water and buy themselves a pair of specs, and Roncador, all gallant in brilliantine and a red bandage on his arm, so bright that when people said to Comandante Brito it was a communist or anarchist or rabble-rousing symbol, Comandante Brito said, actually it's a wine-coloured ribbon in honour of Nossa Senhora da Conceição and we'd do well to respect a citizen's faith, please, friends. And there was Cinco Pernadas, said Tio Balela, a bundle of fury and huff and puff, and when people said to Comandante Brito, my dear Comandante, aren't you going to arrest that dangerous outlaw, he said, it can't be Cinco Pernadas, because Cinco Pernadas died after being stabbed fifteen times on the Canal do Mangue, everyone knows that, this here is Evandro da Silva Berto, a good man and a law-abiding citizen, and well dressed besides.

Lining up to represent the *gringos* were just a bunch of ugly people, said Tio Balela, at least they were until afterwards, when in the post-match celebrations we got to know them inside out. There was Franquarque, short and stocky, arms thicker than his legs, a man who marked forwards so closely that, seen from a distance, it looked like love and courtship, and when he'd gone home the fruits of his visit blossomed and they all had arms thicker than legs and they formed a travelling circus, so I'm told. Alberto Royal, who ran so fast that in one enthusiastic burst of speed he kicked up clouds of dust and came to a halt only when he reached the gates to the São Cristóvão main entrance, and afterwards he took such a shine to a girl in Estácio that I'm told he dreamt up a samba, in a language he didn't even understand, wrote it down on a piece of paper and gave it to her, and it was such a fine samba it's still sung today.

There was Samuel Açougue, said Tio Balela, a man who loved other people's legs so much he seemed determined to take home the shin bones of any player who crossed his path, with or without the ball, and who nearly split Japonês Anastácio in two with an off-the-ball tackle. There was Fred Com-Pé, who performed a somersault in the middle of the pitch, thinking he was Leônidas, and played the rest of the game with a limp, wittering on in that budgie language of theirs, and then there was another called Estildarte, said Tio Balela, who scored a goal with his left foot and another with his left hand, and who, with his matinee looks, became the idol of the Canal do Mangue girls, who flashed their titties at him whenever he went near the touchline, and there was Colunga, who at one point in the game fell on top of Madame Leila Buriti and remained there for over six minutes, forming an obstacle in the middle of the pitch that half the crowd said was the ding-dong of the century and half said was ill-fated love, and either way Padre Macedo gave them his blessing afterwards, much to the delight of everyone in the grocery store.

But the devil himself was Bile Cutão, said Tio Balela. That young buck dressed up a haggard face with a scruffy little goatee and he ran on the tips of his toes with jumps so fleet he looked like a cavy, and he ran and ran and never came to a stop, not even when the ball left the field of play. Bile Cutão was a man of faith, said Tio Balela, for when a cross came over he leapt in the air when the ball was still high in the sky, and the ball seemed to move towards his head out of respect for the audacity of the man, and he was such a good footballer that for every two goals the *gringos* scored, three of them were his. At one point in the game he'd scored four goals in a row and Comandante Brito had to be talked out of arresting him, and even when Lero, Raposo and Mascate hugged hold of his swivelling hips as he burst forward with the ball, the skinny young buck just dragged the poor lads along with him, and almost knocked Rasteiro's head off with his shot.

He was a legend was Bile Cutão, said Tio Balela, and for every goal Rasteiro or Cinco Pernadas scored, Bile Cutão responded in kind, and the *gringo* was so full of cunning and jiggle that an incredulous drunk shouted, that whitey's so good he must be a black albino. Nevertheless, the port team proved a match for the *gringos*. Ecstatic supporters invaded the pitch at the final whistle, raising quaysiders and *gringos* alike aloft, for they were all heroes that day, and we went from grocer's store to liquor store to tavern to bar, and we ended up sitting our backsides down on the pavement outside Young Abrão's as he handed out cachaça and wine and cognac, and he even presented every player with a hat that smelt of fresh leather. The revelry was such that the score got forgotten, said Tio Balela, and even today it's hotly disputed in bars and restaurants from Praça XV to Praça Mauá.

What is known, for it's an established, engraved and undisputed fact, said Tio Balela, is that the dish invented by the English had been reinvented by Brazil, we'd made it our own, ours to feast on. Young Abrão and Old Abrão and Seu Nino would have said the same, and the whole world knew it too, after listening to radio commentators describe, in every language under the sun, the tricks and flicks performed by Leônidas, Domingos, Batatais, Nariz, Britto and the rest of our footballing gods on the brioches of France. Not even the ref who darkened Domingos da Guia's good name by inventing a penalty, blatantly gifting the Italians victory in the semi-final, could undo what had been done that heavenly year of 1938, because we'd all become princes, said Tio Balela, and as the old samba went, let the *gringos* keep their crown, they who have blondes but have no brunettes, for we were all princes and we had a king who'd no need of a crown, and that king was Leônidas da Silva.

From the veranda of their house on Morro da Conceição, Young Abrão and Old Abrão looked out to sea, and they saw the good ship *Arlanza* returning with the golden boys, but they didn't go down to Praça Mauá to welcome it, said Tio Balela. And that's because from their vantage point they could see the *Queen Mary* departing, the very same day Leônidas and his troupe returned. Young Abrão had his father's cap on his head and his father's pipe in his mouth and his father's grandson at his feet, said Tio Balela. According to Seu Nino, Old Abrão asked Young Abrão if one day he too would adventure on the high seas, and father told son that there's no need to, lad, this country has more land to set foot on than the rest of the world has sea to swim in. The sun shone that day, Seu Nino would tell Seu Bahia and me, whenever we dragged out lunch in his tavern, when the *Arlanza* returned all full of smiles, and at my father's feet sat the match ball from when the port beat the *gringos*, the same ball I had encased and put up there on the wall for the whole world to see. That's the ball of Young Abrão and Merle Loide and Old Abrão, of Roncador and Cinco Pernadas and Bile Cutão, of victory and defeat, Seu Nino would say to us, and anyone else who'd listen. And he'd puff out his chest and his eyes would well up with tears, may Seu Bahia be my witness, said Tio Balela, and, boys and girls, he'd say this: that's the ball of the big family that is Brazil.

THE TRANSLATORS

Jonathan Blitzer is on the editorial staff of *The New Yorker* and *Words Without Borders*. His writing has appeared in *The New York Times*, *Prospect*, *The New Republic* and *The Nation*, among other places. When you tell him "football", his first thought is – and may always be – of the pig-skinned sort, but he likes soccer just fine too.

Ruth Clarke is a translator working from Spanish, French and Italian into English. She holds a degree in Modern European Languages from the University of Durham and an MA in Translation Studies from the University of Sheffield. Ruth has translated work by authors from Mexico to Benin, most recently contributing to English PEN's collection of Enoh Meyomesse's poetry *Jail Verse: Poems from Kondengui Prison* and Words Without Borders' Venezuela edition. Ruth has tried adopting football teams from the heights of Argentina's top flight to the bottom of the Spanish third division, but for some reason she always comes back to Sheffield Wednesday.

Currently the Latin American editor of a commercial publication, **Tim Girven** has been engaged with the region for twenty-five years. He is a former Latin American editor of Index on Censorship and reviews editor for *Travesia: A Journal of Latin American Cultural Studies*. In addition to having published in a diverse array of print media, he also works in radio and has produced a series of radio programmes on Latin American subjects for the London-based Resonance104.4fm. A founder of Ragpicker Press and co-editor of *The Football Crónicas*, he's supported Liverpool for nigh on forty years and hopes this will be the year they finally win the Premiership.

Rosalind Harvey's translation of Juan Pablo Villalobos's debut novel *Down the Rabbit Hole* was shortlisted for the Guardian First Book Award and the Oxford-Weidenfeld prize. Her co-translation of Enrique Vila-Matas's *Dublinesque* was shortlisted for the Independent Foreign Fiction prize and has been longlisted for the Dublin IMPAC award. Her latest translation is Villalobos's *Quesadillas*, with And Other Stories. She lives in Bristol and organises translation-related events around the country, and tries to avoid football as much as possible.

Montague Kobbé is a German citizen with a Shakespearean name, born in Caracas, in a country that no longer exists, in a millennium that is long gone. His debut novel *The Night of the Rambler* (Akashic, 2013) earned the first runner-up mention at the Premio Casa de las Américas 2014, and his first collection of flash fiction *Tales of Bed Sheets and Departure Lounges / Historias de camas y aeropuertos* (DogHorn, 2014) features fifty bilingual short stories. He has kept a literary column in Sint Maarten's *The Daily Herald* since 2008, writes about vintage football for the Spanish online magazine fronterad.com and regularly posts castles of English smoke and Spanish mirrors on his blog, *MEMO FROM LA-LA LAND*. As a translator, he controls traffic in both directions between English and Spanish and has had more than a dozen books published, including Spanish cult photographer Alberto García Alix's comprehensive catalogue *From Where There Is No Return* (La Fábrica, 2010), and

The A–Z of Spanish Photographers (La Fábrica, 2014). He's been praying to the gods to watch over Bayern Munich since the days when Madjer's back-heel flick left him crying in the kitchen of his childhood home. Now that the gods are finally listening, he has found in the mighty Arsenal a new source of pain and love, which are one and the same thing.

After graduating in Spanish and French, **Chris Lloyd** climbed aboard a bus from Cardiff to Catalonia and stayed there for over twenty years, working as a teacher, in publishing and as a translator. Now back in Cardiff, he works as a freelance translator and writer. He translates mainly academic and arts texts. He has written a number of books for Rough Guides and his first novel, set in Catalonia, will be published in Catalan translation in 2014. He supports Barça and Wales, which is as good a grounding in experiencing the joys of triumph and disaster as you'll get.

Rachael McGill writes drama and prose and translates from French, German and Spanish. Her translations of the plays *Marieluise* and *Time of the Tortoise* by Kerstin Specht are published by Oberon. Translations of short stories and journalism by Mexican, German, Algerian and Senegalese writers are published in *Mauerreise/Wall Journey* (Steidl, 2010). She is boycotting the World Cup.

Robin Patterson translates from Portuguese and is currently working on his first book-length translation, *Nosso Musseque* by the Angolan novelist José Luandino Vieira, to be published by Dedalus Books. He is a member of the And Other Stories Portuguese reading group and has translated samples for a number of publishers, authors and literary agencies. Robin has participated in several literary translation summer schools and was mentored by Margaret Jull Costa as part of the British Centre for Literary Translation's 2013 mentorship programme. He once lived with a couple of ardent Arsenal fans in the shadows of the old Highbury stadium and so considers himself an honorary Gooner, at least when they're winning.

Jethro Soutar is an English writer and a translator of Spanish and Portuguese. He has written two works of non-fiction with a Latin American theme (*Ronaldinho: Football's Flamboyant Maestro* and *Gael García Bernal and the Latin American New Wave*), both published by Anova Books. He has translated Argentinian and Brazilian crime fiction for Bitter Lemon Press, and his translation of *By Night the Mountain Burns* by Juan Tomás Ávila Laurel will be published by And Other Stories in late 2014. He is co-editor of *The Football Crónicas* and a founder of Ragpicker Press. He was taken to see Sheffield United draw 0-0 with Brentford aged four; he has since seen them lose four play-off finals and four FA Cup semi-finals.

OTHER CONTRIBUTORS:

Tim Vickery is an English football journalist who has lived in Brazil since 1994. He is South American football correspondent for the BBC, writes a weekly column for sambafoot.com and participates in The World Football Phone-In, which airs weekly as part of *Up All Night* on BBC Radio 5 Live on Saturday mornings. His Twitter feed is @Tim_Vickery

ACKNOWLEDGEMENTS

Proceeds from this book will be donated to The Bottletop Foundation, a UK-based organisation that does outstanding work empowering young people in Africa and Brazil, tackling sensitive issues including the prevention of HIV/Aids, unplanned teenage pregnancy, substance abuse, gender inequality, low self-esteem and vocational-skills deficits (http://bottletop.org/pages/foundation).

Authors, translators and editors provided their services for free, and designers, copy editors, typesetters and proofreaders worked below market rates, in order to keep production costs to a minimum and donations to a maximum. Ragpicker Press would like to thank them all for their time, energy and generosity.

Ragpicker Press coordinated a crowdfunding campaign to raise the funds to produce the book. As part of the campaign, we commissioned fifteen artists to produce fifteen artworks inspired by the fifteen texts in *The Football Crónicas*. The project was brilliantly coordinated by Eva Oddo, and we are immensely grateful to her and the following artists, all of whom lent their talents to the project for free: Luísa Alpalhão, Melaina Barnes, Eva Bensasson, David Caldwell, Eamonn Campbell, Paula Claudio, Wolfgang Fuetterer, David Kiely, Michelle Letowska, Zoran Lucić, Morag MacInnes, Ryan McGoverne, Ernesto Muñiz, Gustavo Nóbrega, Robert Worley. We also thank Paul McNaught, Richard Owusu-Awuah, Kalaf Angelo and Denise Mina for their contributions to the crowdfunding project,

Michael Ng for his work on the Ragpicker website, and Alexandre Agabiti Fernandez, Pablo García Guerrero, Rogelio Villarreal and Sergio Olguín for their help along the way.

The crowdfunding project attracted ninety-three backers, without whose support the whole thing would have been impossible. We are very grateful to all our backers, especially Alexandra Vilas-Bôas, Alex Marston, Andreas Loizou, Andreia Andrade dos Santos Gomes, Ben Stuart, Colin Doig, Daniel Hahn, David and Helen Smith, Elisabeth Weise, Francisco Pizarro, Francisco Vilhena, Gwyn Roberts, Ian Soutar and Kathy Loizou, Louise Pryde, Luis Naia, Jacob Aitken, Jim Blackburn, Joanna Thomas, Joanne Gillespie, John Clarke, John Gilbertson, John McGill, Josie Soutar, Maggie Soutar and Geoff Rowe, Neil Soutar, Rhys Thomas, Richard Cotton, Rob McGowan, Sam Dubberley, Steve Callanan, Víctor García Guerrero, Yasmin Khan and Zoe Perry.